REMEMBER ME

CHARITY NORMAN was born in Uganda and brought up in successive draughty vicarages in Yorkshire and Birmingham. After several years' travel she became a barrister, specialising in crime and family law in the northeast of England. Also a mediator and telephone crisis line listener, she's passionate about the power of communication to slice through the knots. In 2002, realising that her three children had barely met her, she took a break from the law and moved with her family to Aotearoa New Zealand. Her first novel, *Freeing Grace*, was published in 2010. *Second Chances* (*After the Fall*) was a Richard and Judy Book Club choice and World Book Night title. Her most recent, *The Secrets of Strangers*, was a BBC Radio 2 Book Club choice for 2020, shortlisted for Best Crime Novel in the Ngaio Marsh Awards for Crime Fiction, and for best International Crime Fiction in the Ned Kelly Awards.

Also by Charity Norman

Freeing Grace

After the Fall

The Son-in-Law

The New Woman

See You in September

The Secrets of Strangers

REMEMBER ME

ME

Charity Norman

ALLEN&UNWIN

First published in Australia and New Zealand in 2022 by Allen & Unwin

First published in Great Britain in 2022 by Allen & Unwin, an imprint of
Atlantic Books Ltd.

1 2 3 4 5 6 7 8 9

A CIP catalogue record for this book is available from the British Library.

Paperback ISBN: 978 1 83895 418 5
E-book ISBN: 978 1 83895 419 2

Printed in Great Britain

Allen & Unwin
An Imprint of Atlantic Books Ltd
Ormond House, 26–27 Boswell Street
London WC1N 3JZ

www.allenandunwin.com/uk

MIX
Paper from
responsible sources
FSC® C171272

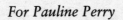

For Pauline Perry

Remember me, remember me, but ah! forget my fate.

—Henry Purcell, *Dido and Aeneas*

17 June 1994

'I envy you,' she says.

She doesn't. Why would she envy me? She's Dr Leah Parata, five years older and infinitely, effortlessly superior. Everything about the woman screams energy and competence, even the way she's twirling that turquoise beanie around her index finger. She's tall, light on her feet, all geared up for back-country hiking in a black jacket—or maybe navy blue, as I'll later tell the police. Waterproof trousers, walking boots with red laces. Hair in a heavy plait, though a few dark tendrils have escaped.

'I really do,' she insists. 'You've bought your ticket to Ecuador. What an adventure.'

'Hope so.'

'I know so.' She grabs a bar of Cadbury's from the display and holds it up to show me. 'Got a craving.'

'I didn't know you were a chocoholic.'

'Just when it's cold. This should keep me going all the way to Biddulph's.'

I've only once managed to haul myself up to Biddulph's bivvy, a ramshackle hut on the bush line, built about a hundred years ago for professional rabbiters. They must have been hardy people. As I count her change, I peer out at the weather: standing water on the petrol station forecourt, raindrops bouncing high off the mustard-coloured paintwork of her car. The ranges are smothered in charcoal cloud, as though some monstrous creature is breathing out giant plumes of smoke.

'Seriously?' I ask. 'You're heading up there? Today?'

She takes a casual glance at the cloud cover. It seems to delight her. 'Lucky me, eh? Perfect weather for finding Marchant's snails. The first wet days after a dry spell bring 'em out. I've got a happy weekend ahead of me, crawling around in the leaf litter.'

I can't imagine why anyone would choose to tramp through those rain-soaked forests and uplands, but then I've never been a mountain woman. Leah is, of course. She took her very first steps in the Ruahine Range. To her, that wilderness is home. She's going on and on about her snails while I smile and nod.

'They're *this* big!'—holding up her fingers to demonstrate. 'Carnivorous.' She catches me blanching at the image of a giant, flesh-eating snail. 'Okay, maybe not the sexiest of our native creatures. But their shells are works of art, they've been around for millions of years, and now they're in trouble because everything preys on them. Possums, rats, pigs.'

Blah blah blah, I think, because I'm twenty-one, and empty-headed, and I've been jealous of Leah for as long as I can remember. Her teeth are a bit crooked. She has a high forehead, a small mole on her left cheekbone and a permanent concentration crease, a vertical line between her eyebrows. Yet somehow, these imperfections add to the hypnotic effect. I can see why my brother Eddie's had a crush since he first clapped eyes on her, swimming her horse in the Arapito stream. They were both eleven then, and he was a scrawny kid from Leeds, but he still hasn't given up hope.

Just as she's opening the door to leave the shop, she drops her chocolate—*oops*—and swiftly stoops to pick it up again, flashing a wide, warm smile at me.

'Ecuador! Good for you, Emily.'

'I'll see you before I go,' I call after her.

I'm not sure she's heard me. She's striding across the flooded forecourt, pulling her beanie onto her head. The turquoise looks vivid even through rain-streaming glass. She checks her watch before getting into the car. I bet she's already forgotten our conversation. She'll be thinking about her snails, about what she's got to achieve over the weekend.

Her brake lights flicker at the exit. Now she's accelerating away, water rising in sheets as her wheels bounce through the flooded hollows.

•

They never found Leah Parata. Not a boot, not a backpack, not a turquoise beanie. After she left me that day, she vanished off the face of the earth.

ONE

February 2019

The sign I painted thirty years ago still hung beside the road gate: *Arapito*. The name means 'End of the path', which seemed eerily apt right now. I'd illustrated it with a pair of fantails in flight, though time and rust had obliterated all but their wings. Leaning out of the driver's window, I opened the creaking metal mouth of the mailbox. Mainly junk. A bank statement.

The landscape was a bleached desert, acres of desiccated grassland even up here in the foothills. Dust billowed in a beige cloud as I nosed my car up the drive. A small flock of sheep sprinted ahead, tightly bunched together, docked tails bouncing. Familiar things: the school bus shelter at the gate, the derelict woolshed, the backdrop of mountains. At the end of the drive a long, single-storey villa, surrounded by trees, clad in white weatherboards with heat haze dancing off its tin roof. *Arapito*. My home.

Dad was standing on the back porch, wearing canvas trousers and a polo shirt. Upright, tidy, self-contained. I waved as I rounded the house. I waved again, smiling, once I'd cut my engine. He simply watched me, shielding his eyes with one hand.

5

Silence. For one final breath, I hadn't quite arrived. I was still on my journey, still free. I had a desperate impulse to turn the key, reverse and speed away—back to the airport, back to my own life.

Why was I here? What possessed me?

I was here because of that phone call. Just a month ago, a wake-up call. I'd worked in my studio all day, gone out on the town to celebrate a friend's promotion, fallen into bed long after midnight. Four hours later, the blaring of my phone dragged me from the paralysis of dream.

Still dark, silly o'clock. Must be Nathan, calling from . . . Malaysia? No, he'd moved on. Jakarta. My son never worried too much about what time it was in London, especially when he'd run out of money and wanted a payout from the Bank of Mum.

'Nath? Whassup?' My tongue was still numbed by sleep.

Not Nathan. My caller was a woman.

'Oh, Emily, I'm so sorry! Have I woken you?'

I lay with my eyes shut, trying to place the voice. A New Zealander, for sure. I wasn't in touch with many people in Tawanui, and these deep, placid tones certainly didn't belong to my sister. Carmen always sounds as though she's about to slap someone's face.

'I forgot the time difference,' the woman said.

Ah! Now I had it. Raewyn Parata. Our neighbour, our school bus driver. Leah's mother, the woman whose name was synonymous with tragedy. Raewyn had ample reason to be angry with the world and yet she always sounded pretty much as she did now: interested, gently determined.

Something must be wrong with Dad. I couldn't remember when I last lifted the phone to call him. Damn it, I meant to! If the worst had happened, I'd fly back for the funeral. Be easier to talk to him when he's dead.

I didn't say any of that. You don't. You observe the social niceties, even when you know bad news is coming.

'Raewyn! How are you?'

'Good. I'm good.'

I was pulling a jersey over my head, feeling guilty, thinking about funerals.

'What's happened? Something up with Dad?'

'Well . . .' A hesitation. 'You heard about his accident?'

'Accident?'

'Nobody's told you. Uh-huh. Thought not. About a week ago, he and his car somehow ended up in a ditch next to Arapito Road. He wasn't hurt—just bruises—but they kept him in Hastings hospital overnight in case he was concussed. Ira dragged his car out of the ditch and took it to the panelbeater. Anyway, it's not just that . . . um, where do I start? For quite a while now I've been bringing him meals, shopping, doing a bit of cleaning.'

'He can afford a cleaner, Raewyn.'

'That's not the point.'

'You shouldn't be cleaning for him.'

It's tricky to pull on your jeans with a phone tucked under your chin. I managed it somehow before blundering into the kitchen. *Tea. Milk.* I pictured Raewyn in her own kitchen, on the other side of the planet. She stayed on after her son Ira moved out—stayed on alone, despite the shadows gathered there. A wooden house with peeling paint and rotting boards; fruit trees in the garden, generations of sheep grazing up to the fence.

'The doctors were worried,' she was saying. 'He kept asking how he'd got there. He was trying to examine other patients, checking their charts! We've known for ages, haven't we?'

'Have we?'

'But—oh, Felix!—he's refusing to take any medication. He says he's not going to prolong the inevitable.'

'He was fine when I was last home.'

'Are you sure about that?' I heard the small silence of her disapproval. 'That was . . .'

'Getting on for three years ago, now.'

'Long time. He was already hiding it then. Battling on. That's why he resigned from everything, that's why he's become such a recluse. Manu did the same: quietly gave things up when he knew he couldn't manage.'

The fridge door closed with a gentle click. It was covered in photos, mainly of Nathan at every stage from babyhood to twenty-two. Nathan, the cleverest little knock-kneed toddler who ever lived. Ten-year-old Nathan whizzing down the slide in our local playground. My favourite was quite a recent one of the two of us, skating on the Somerset House ice rink with our arms linked.

And there was Nathan with his grandfather on the porch at Arapito. Dad looked handsome in his gardening hat, neatly shaved, Mediterranean-blue eyes in a face that somehow seemed both delicate and heavy. Nathan was a nineteen-year-old beanpole with copper hair, freckles and glasses. My father and my son both stood very straight, wearing their photo smiles, awkward grins they stuck on whenever a camera was pointed at them.

I held my forefinger to my lips, pressing the kiss onto the beloved boy in the picture. I took this photo as we were setting out for the airport, the last time I saw Dad. He looked perfectly normal. I didn't remember anything . . . oh. Yes, I did, come to think of it. Little eccentricities, just a few wacky moments. He tried to serve us frozen green beans instead of ice cream. And there was that day he nipped into town to get milk but came back hours later with no shopping at all. He seemed angry, said he'd been collared by an old patient who talked so much that Dad had completely forgotten what he'd come for. Nathan called him an absent-minded professor. Now that I thought back, perhaps he wasn't angry. Perhaps he was frightened.

'They did tests at the hospital,' Raewyn said. 'They got him to see a consultant.'

'And?'

'I'm afraid they think it's Alzheimer's.'

Alzheimer's. Among people my age—the sandwich generation, squashed between parents and children, never quite coping with either and feeling constantly inadequate—the word had friends recoiling with grimaces and sympathetic tuts. *Oh no! I'm so sorry, that's a cruel thing.* We're all afraid it's coming for us too. We're all terrified when we forget someone's name.

Raewyn was talking about the diagnosis, about what it meant for Dad.

'They've told him he has to stop driving,' she said. 'He's given me his car keys in case he forgets.'

'No! How's he meant to manage? You guys live miles out of town.'

'The thing is, Emily, this isn't new. He forgets to pay his bills. His electricity got cut off. I've even found him gardening in his pyjamas at midday.'

This, somehow, was more upsetting than his driving into a ditch. I couldn't imagine my father in any state other than that of immaculate dignity. He always—*always*—wore a jacket and tie to work, his shirt collars literally starched, a Panama hat for gardening.

'Today was the final straw for me,' Raewyn said. 'I went round with his shopping. I'd only just walked in when a frying pan burst into flames. These wooden houses can turn into infernos within minutes.'

'Do Carmen and Eddie know about this diagnosis?' My siblings.

'They do now. I don't think they were surprised.'

'So what's the plan?'

'They both lead such busy lives. They think he needs to go into a care home, probably St Patrick's, but he won't hear of it.

That's why I'm phoning you, Emily. You're the one person I could think of who might be able and willing to help.'

I indulged in a moment of smugness at being the *one* person— but I could see exactly where all of this was leading, and I didn't want to go there.

'I think you should come home for a while,' she said.

There it was.

'I don't live in the next town,' I reminded her.

'I know that.'

'I don't even live in the same hemisphere.' I sounded like a petulant teenager. I *felt* like one. 'I'll phone him today, I promise. But I can't simply drop everything, and there's the cost.'

'Imagine if you never got to say goodbye.'

Raewyn knew all about saying goodbye; she knew about never having the chance to say it. Manu. Leah.

'My useless brother and sister are both twelve thousand miles closer,' I moaned.

The kitchen door was inching open. A chubby-faced tabby squeezed through the gap and made a beeline for his bowl of biscuits. Max, my lodger's cat. My good friend, who spent his mornings curled up on a cushion in my cramped little studio. He was the model for Admiral Flufflebum, a wise, kind cat who lived in Buckingham Palace in a series of books I illustrated, whose success helped to pay the mortgage on this flat.

Raewyn aimed another shot.

'Come and see him while he still knows you, Emily. Don't just come for his funeral.'

'We're not very close.'

'You love him, though.'

After we'd hung up, I sat at the table and tried to kid myself that my father wasn't my responsibility. A bus came gliding past, early-morning commuters on the upper deck gazing straight into my world, and I into theirs. Nathan was gone, and the nest felt empty. Christmas was a tinsel-strewn memory. The truly dark days of winter were just beginning: January, February. Rain and greyness and political division.

But it was summer in New Zealand. Temperatures in the thirties, endless blue skies, evening dips in the Arapito stream— our deliciously clear little river, with its pools and cliffs and pockets of native bush.

You love him, though.

I was ten, charging around the house, looking for my gym bag, screaming at Eddie that he'd messed with my effing stuff— and he was screaming back that he hadn't touched my effing stuff, he wouldn't touch it with an effing barge pole, and Mum was slumped on the porch in her housecoat, smoking bitterly, and Carmen was cleaning her muddy riding boots among the cereal bowls on the kitchen table, and it was always like this—always, *always*, every morning. Dad was dressed for work after his run, looking about ten years younger than his wife, who was creased around all her edges. He behaved as though his family were characters on the telly, and he wasn't even watching the show. He wasn't abusive; he was simply absent. He didn't seem to care.

You love him, though.

But maybe he didn't love me. Or any individual, for that matter. My father loved his Fellow Man, whoever the hell that was.

Max jumped onto my lap and began kneading. He had it good: his bed, his bowl and a Burmese playmate who lived two doors down.

'Lucky sod, Max,' I whispered, as he rubbed his cheek against mine. 'Nobody expects you to drop everything for your old man.'

And then I opened my laptop. *Flights. Heathrow–Auckland.*

Not that I was planning on actually . . . I mean, *obviously* not. I was wondering what a flight cost nowadays, that's all. Just out of interest.

•

I opened the car door. Heat surged into my air-conditioned sanctuary, along with the scents of childhood: pasture, sheep dung,
resinous eucalypts and macrocarpas in the shelter belt. The
dry hissing of cicadas reverberated, as though I were inside a
tolling bell.

Dad was still standing on the porch. I inherited my colouring
from him, blue eyes and mid-brown hair, though his had turned
cotton-wool white in recent years. It was a bit out of control right
now, frothing around his head like Einstein's. That wasn't normal
for him.

'Whew—made it!' I cried, walking around to the boot to drag
out my bags.

It was odd that he hadn't greeted me. He wasn't the kind
of father you dash up to and fling your arms around and kiss
noisily, doing a little dance together. He wasn't that kind of father;
I wasn't that kind of daughter. He didn't *do* touching, never had.
But this silence was strange.

Thank goodness for his dogs, who made a fuss of me—pouring
down the steps to say hello, tails waving. First was Gloria, the boss,
an elderly labrador with a coat the colour of shortbread. The smaller
one, Gyp, was given to Dad by one of his many grateful patients.
He had some spaniel in him, and some foxie, and a truckload of
charm—chocolate and white, with bed hair and a lolling tongue.

'Good to see you guys,' I muttered, crouching to ruffle their
ears. 'Gyp, you're all grown up!'

'Morning,' Dad said politely. 'Can I help?'

His smile was too sweet, too empty, too anxious. 'Sweet',
'empty' and 'anxious' were not words I'd ever have used to
describe this man. There was an imposter in my father's body.

'Hey, Dad!' I was laughing to cover the awfulness. 'It's me.
Emily.'

I counted to three before he turned into himself again. The
lights came on, and there he was.

'Emily! Of course it is! Sorry . . . the sun in my eyes, couldn't quite see . . . didn't recognise your car. Hired, is it? No need for that, you can use mine. Well, marvellous, you're here.'

We both pretended it hadn't happened. We both acted out a charade in order to cover up the horrifying fact that a father had failed to recognise his daughter. I climbed the steps to give the token half-hug and air kiss.

'Good journey?' he asked.

'Seems to get longer every time.'

Wariness froze his features again. I don't think he had a clue where I lived.

'I flew from London,' I explained, helping him out, 'into Auckland. Then another flight to Hawke's Bay airport in Napier, and then I drove for an hour down to here.'

'Sounds exhausting.' He gestured towards the house. 'Tea? Coffee? Let me carry your case.'

As he led the way inside, he twice glanced back over his shoulder as though checking I was still there. Perhaps he thought I might be imaginary.

'Good journey?' he asked again.

I blinked. 'Um, yes. Long.'

He tried to make tea, but after he'd opened the same cupboard three times I took over. He stepped aside and let me do it.

'Of course, the mugs are there!' he murmured. 'Stupid of me. Thank you. How was your journey?'

'Fine, Dad. Just a bit long.'

The kitchen hadn't changed in decades: old joinery, high ceiling, blissfully shaded after the glare of the road. A quick trip to the bathroom proved that hadn't changed either. Yellow tiles and a mouldy shower curtain.

Something was filling the air with cooking smells—wine and mushrooms. I lifted the lid of an electric crockpot to reveal a gently bubbling stew.

'You're a chef!' I exclaimed.

'Raewyn brought that round, I think. Biscuits too—here, have one. They're those special biscuits, you know . . . Tip of my tongue. Named after the troops.'

'Anzac?'

'Anzac!'

I was rummaging in the cutlery drawer, looking for a teaspoon. I'd just found one when something caught my eye: a post-it note taped to the handle of the tin opener:

CAN OPENER
1. *Open the metal arms.*
2. *Put cutting edge onto edge of can.*
3. *Press down HARD!*
4. *Turn handle.*

Dad's handwriting used to be controlled and even, marching along straight lines. Much like the man himself, in fact. This was certainly his writing, but it looked as though he'd used his left hand, with quavering wobbles on every letter. Looking around me, I spotted more notes with spidery instructions: on the microwave, the dishwasher, the rice cooker. I slammed the drawer shut. This was terrifying.

'So,' I began, with fake brightness, 'how've you been?'

'Fine fettle.'

'I hear you had a bit of a mishap in your car?'

He looked both guarded and offended, shaking his head with pursed lips.

'Just a small one?' I persisted. 'An argument with a ditch. Didn't you have a night in hospital?'

'A night in . . . ? Ha!' he scoffed. 'Wherever did you hear that rubbish? No, no. An hour. They were fussing about concussion. Do they think I wouldn't recognise concussion in myself?'

'Best to be thorough.'

'Can't have been much of an accident. The car hasn't a scratch on it.'

I decided not to mention the panelbeater. Fetching milk, I found the fridge festooned with notes, all in that wobbly handwriting. One bore Raewyn's phone number, with directions to her house. She and Dad had been neighbours for forty years, she lived just down the track—less than half a mile away, as the crow flies. He could have walked to her place blindfolded.

The other notes were equally disturbing:

DO NOT TALK to man who phones about my COMPUTER FEED DOGS! FOOD IN BAG UNDER SHELF IN STOREROOM
Felix, have you had a shower today?
BRUSH TEETH
CHECK is the OVEN OFF? THE GAS?

One was in red felt tip, with giant letters:

EMILY ARRIVING ABOUT 12 PM MONDAY.
HER ROOM IS READY.
RAEWYN WILL BRING STEW IN CROCKPOT.

A trapdoor was opening under my feet. This wasn't right. What you have to understand is that my father, Felix Kirkland, was the most precise, orderly individual that ever walked this earth. Can you imagine what it's like to be the child of a perfect human being? Now he needed reminders to brush his teeth, to feed his dogs, to greet his daughter when she flew across the world to see him.

We sat in the shade of the broad porch roof, in the low-slung wooden chairs that had been there forever, our tray on the coffee table Eddie made at school: solid, with an inlaid chessboard on its surface. The porch ran right along the back of the house with the boot room at one end. From here we looked over the garden, across steeply undulating farmland to the ranges beyond. I noticed a supply of split logs stacked against the wall, ready for autumn.

The dogs stretched themselves at Dad's feet while we humans made conversation about the dry weather, the state of the garden— 'Needs a bit of attention,' Dad mumbled, shaking his head at the overgrown bushes, clumps of parched grass on the drive. None of this neglect would have mattered at all, but it wasn't him.

Stilted and impersonal conversation, on the other hand, *was* him. It always had been. This was why I only made the journey every few years. The twins had both settled in Auckland, while I'd run even further.

After a long silence, Dad put down his teacup.

'I want to get my house in order,' he announced. 'I mean literally. *This* house. Papers and rubbish all over my study. I can't seem to get rid of anything.'

This I could believe. His only vice was to be a hoarder of documents.

'You don't have to get rid of anything, Dad.'

'I do!' He slammed his hands onto his thighs. 'But I can't seem to make any progress. It's so irritating.'

'It doesn't matter.'

'I can't leave all this mess for other people to deal with.'

'Nobody will mind.'

'I *must* get my house in order.' He was looking at me hopefully, half-smiling. 'You'll help me, Emily? You'll help me?'

My throat had closed. Maybe it was jetlag and sleep deprivation, maybe the treacherous weepiness of perimenopause, maybe just the fact of being home after three years and knowing that this visit really might be the last.

But I think it was because it was the first time in my life—the very first time, so far as I could remember—that my father had asked for my help.

TWO

After lunch, Dad retreated to his study. He claimed to have letters to write but his eyelids were drooping. I suspected he'd be writing in his dreams, slumped in his armchair.

I wandered around the dark rooms of Arapito homestead, reacquainting myself with its slumbering stillness. The house smelled exactly as it always had: of dust, of history, of slow disintegration, all overlaid with some kind of polish—which was odd, since I'd never seen anyone actually polish anything. The glass in the sash windows was warped, their frames excavated by wood-boring insects. The grandmother clock kept a steady heartbeat, chiming the quarter-hours as it had throughout my childhood. It lived in the snug, a comfortable little room connected to the kitchen by an archway. I sat on the sofa for a time, watching the pendulum.

I'd talked to my brother and sister before booking my flights. They presented a united front. Par for the course.

'We're trying to persuade Dad to set up an EPOA,' said Carmen, who had just been down to see him.

'A what?'

'An enduring power of attorney. We need to safeguard his finances.'

'Against what?'

'Anyone who might take advantage of him.'

'Yeah?' Something in her tone had me bristling. 'Like who?'

'Just whoever. And we need to be able to make decisions about his care going forward. It's really difficult to know what to do. We're thinking about St Patrick's.'

Tawanui's rest home. Bahamas-heated, urine-scented. Dad used to be on the management board, and GP to most of the residents. He founded a gardening club and a choir; he often took the latest of his succession of labradors with him on visits. I saw blank faces brighten, arthritic fingers reaching to stroke soft fur. Dad knew all about St Pat's.

As the clock chimed, I slid in and out of sleep. Two am in England. Ringing in my ears, gravel behind my eyelids. *Must stay awake.* If I succumbed now, I'd be making cups of tea half the night.

Moments later I was heading across the paddocks towards Raewyn's house, my sandals scuffing on bone-dry grass. Gyp and Gloria trotted beside me, stopping to drink from troughs on the way. At one stage I spotted Ira Parata in the far distance, a white-helmeted figure on a quad bike. I jumped about and waved, but he passed out of sight without seeing me.

Ira and I lived in one another's pockets when we were small, chanting and giggling on the back seat of the school bus while our older siblings pretended not to know us—*Leah and Eddie sitting in a tree, K-I-S-S-I-N-G! First comes love, then comes marriage, then comes a baby in a—*

Dear Lord, poor Eddie. He used to turn crimson, right to the tips of his ears. Leah just smiled and shook her head.

Kids were dropped home in ones and twos as Raewyn fought the massive steering wheel, navigating slippery tracks and steep hills. By the time she turned up Arapito Road, only the five of us were left: two Paratas, three Kirklands. Ira and Leah often got off at our place, leaving Raewyn to drive on alone and face the grimness of Manu's illness. Leah and the twins did their homework together. They were all swots. Eddie's only ambition—apart from getting Leah to go out with him—was to be a doctor like Dad, but he didn't get the grades.

I heard a yell of greeting as I opened Raewyn's gate, and the wonderfully familiar figure came pelting to envelop me in her arms. Relief took my breath away. Someone normal, someone whose mind wasn't sliding away into the ether. She smelled of soap and butter. For the second time that day, my throat felt as though it had a knot tied in it.

'Oh dear.' She peered into my face. 'Was he in a state?'

'He didn't know who I was.'

She tutted, holding my hands in both of hers.

'He was so polite.' I laughed miserably, trying to shift the ache in my throat. 'He said, *Can I help you?*'

'I should have been there.'

'You tried to warn me.'

The dogs lay panting in the shade of an apple tree. Raewyn took my arm and guided me towards the house, her head on a level with my shoulder. She was barefoot, wearing a man's checked shirt and baggy khaki shorts, silver-grey hair hanging halfway to her waist.

'He was sharp as a tack this morning,' she said. 'I left him in the study, sorting through the newsletters from St Patrick's.' She bent down to pick a shiny strawberry and passed it to me. 'Imagine if he fetches up in their dementia unit, among all those other lost souls.'

'D'you think he knows what's happening to him?'

'Sometimes. Two or three years ago, he told me he was losing the battle. He was going to become a blank sheet in the end. Tears pouring down his cheeks. *God help me. God help me, Raewyn. I'll be erased.* But now he seems to have accepted it.'

I had only ever once seen my father cry. Once, in all the years.

'He's only seventy-five,' I protested. 'He was still hiking in the ranges last time I was over. He never loses a game of chess, he's been on the board of half the non-profits in the district. I thought you could avoid dementia if you kept your mind and body in shape.'

'Maybe he's bought himself more time by keeping so active? C'mon out of this heat.'

She straightened, holding a handful of strawberries in the palm of her hand, and I followed her up the wooden ramp to her back door. The ramp was installed decades earlier for Manu's wheelchair, along with widened doorways and a special shower.

Stepping into Raewyn's kitchen felt like another homecoming: the sense of order, the faded linoleum on the floor, that lingering smell of tomato plants and baking. While she poured cold drinks, I looked at the photos lined up along her dresser. I knew them well. A triptych of Leah: a teenager in white judo gear, a mountain climber on a peak. The third was taken during her PhD graduation ceremony. She was regal in a magnificent korowai— a Māori cloak—with a mortarboard balanced on her mass of corkscrew curls; that intense gaze, the vertical crease on her brow. She had her whole life ahead of her.

There were photos of her dad, too. Nice man. One showed him in his prime, lean and muscled, stooping to shear a sheep on the boards of a woolshed and looking startlingly like Ira. The image was faded, too small for its brass frame. I had a dim recollection of Manu in those earliest days: a cheerful farmer in a sunhat and shorts and big boots, chatting across the fence to whichever of my parents was in our garden. Sometimes he'd take Ira and me across the farm, bouncing around on the flatbed of his truck.

The other photo of Manu was upsetting. I would never have believed it could be the same person if I hadn't witnessed his decline myself. A wasted doll, propped in a high-backed armchair in the Paratas' front room. Someone had put a yellow paper crown on his head. I'm sure it was meant to look festive, but it seemed like mockery as it slid down his emaciated skull. His hair was shorn, because his constant movement left it matted. His body seemed twisted, his mouth wide open, head tilted backwards so that he stared up at the ceiling.

I spoke to him—in that chair, on that day, wearing that yellow crown. His last Christmas. He couldn't form words, but I think he tried to smile at me. The writhing that had tortured him for years was less now, though he still flung his limbs about—even, Raewyn told me, when he was sleeping. She'd lined his bed with sheepskin so that he wasn't bruised at night. He was struggling to swallow, and there was talk of his need for specialist care, but there were so few beds and nowhere close by. While they were waiting, his heart began to fail. Dad arranged palliative care. Manu died in March 1992, with his family around him.

Raewyn was in the photo too: perched on an arm of the chair, clutching Manu's thin hand. Her trademark flame-red mane was turning grey. Leah sat on the other side, pressing her cheek to her father's, gazing straight at the camera. Such a contrast: her vitality, his vacancy. Ira stood scowling behind them all. He hated having his photo taken. Brother and sister would have been nineteen and twenty-four at the time, but living very different lives. He'd stayed at home to run the farm and look after his dad. She was a high-flyer, a doctoral student with a scholarship, following her dreams. Nobody suggested *she* should sacrifice her future. Didn't seem fair to me. Though as things turned out, she didn't have a future.

'How's Ira?' I asked now. 'I caught a glimpse of him when I was walking over.'

'Good. He's . . . yes, I think he's good.'

That was the stock response around here. It meant nothing. Everyone was always 'good', until they weren't.

Raewyn picked up the picture, dusted it against her shirt.

'He's forty-six years old, he lives alone in the single man's quarters, he works from dawn till dusk every day of the week— except when he gets drunk as a skunk at the Tawanui pub. Most of his friends are fathers now, some even granddads.' She glanced out of the window, in the direction of Ira's place. 'I know he won't have children in case he passes on the Huntington's gene. Breaks my heart a bit. But surely there are women out there who'd settle down with him, love him for himself?'

I was sure there were plenty. The odd girlfriend had come and gone from Ira's life, but he'd never let one get close.

'Can't *you* save him, Emily?' asked Raewyn. 'You were always partners in crime.'

I chuckled. 'Blind leading the blind.'

Ten-year-old me had blithely assumed that Ira and I would get married one day. I'd thought he was so handsome, with his dark curls, his shining eyes and that confident lift to his chin. I used to daydream about our house, our puppies, the pet lambs we'd feed. None of it came true. My best mate and I never even dated, never kissed, never so much as held hands except to haul one another up onto the roof of Manu's woolshed.

'Whenever he can spare a day from the farm, he heads up into the ranges,' said Raewyn. 'He claims to be hunting, and he'll come home with venison, but I know he's looking for his sister.'

'Still looking? It's been . . .'

'Twenty-five years this coming June. There won't be anything left of her to find.'

Raewyn's gaze was drawn towards a narrow saddle between two peaks, easily identifiable by the livid scar of a slip. I knew Biddulph's bivvy lay close to that point, just below the bush line.

At this distance, the uplands might have been bare rock, shimmering in mirror-bright blue.

I'd been up there. The Ruahine Range is a biodiversity hotspot, one of the last refuges for all kinds of native plants and creatures, including Leah's giant snail. Our school used to take us on summer camps, yahooing our way up easy, well-marked trails through the rainforest, stopping to snack on bags of scroggin and making so much racket that we barely heard the trickling of the streams or the strange calls of the birds. We'd sleep in a modern hut with gas, foam mattresses and glass in the windows. Our teachers would nag us about not wandering off—*they'll never find you*—and not dropping litter. We used torches when we crept out to the long-drop toilet at night, so we never even saw the exploding majesty of the stars.

I'd only once been more adventurous. When I was thirteen, I asked Dad to take me with him on one of his hikes. I was inspired by Ira's memories of camping with Manu and Leah, and imagined long conversations as we strolled through the bush, perhaps lighting a fire in a cosy hut.

We made a day trip to Biddulph's, which Dad said was a 'manageable walk for someone not very fit'. I was so excited. I got ready the night before, and we left early. Well, what a nightmare! All I remember is screaming limbs and lungs as I scrambled up that hellishly steep trail. Dad seemed to dance from rock to rock across a gushing stream, but I fell and was soaked. When we finally reached it, the hut was grim: no fireplace, no water, just a couple of rotting canvas bunks and a packing case for a table. Rat droppings everywhere. I almost cried. I longed to get home to flat ground, a hot shower and a sofa. On the way back down, Dad apologised. *I overestimated your fitness*, he said. *My mistake. I'm sorry.*

I felt such a hopeless failure. I hadn't been good enough; I would *never* be good enough. Not like Leah.

Raewyn turned from the window. 'How long can you stay?'

'Three weeks.'

She folded her arms, lowering her chin so that it tripled. I knew that look.

'Leave me alone, Raewyn,' I protested. 'You can't expect me to hang about until . . . I mean, he could outlive me. How about some home help for him? I'll look into it.'

'You've got a Kiwi passport, right? I bet you can work from here.'

'Theoretically, for a while. But it's—'

She was clapping her hands. 'Hooray!'

'No, *not* hooray. I don't work in a vacuum; it's a collaborative process. I need to have face-to-face conversations, I need to provide original work, I need—'

She wasn't interested in my excuses. She pointed out that we had the internet nowadays, and all kinds of snazzy equipment. She often video-chatted with her great-nieces and nephews.

'Felix has given his whole life to others,' she declared. 'Will nobody give anything back now?'

When I mentioned Eddie and Carmen, she flapped a dismissive hand.

'We both know they're not going to turn their lives upside down for him. Even if they wanted to offer him a home, I can't see Rhonda or Richard being very happy. And anyway, poor Felix! Imagine being bossed about by Carmen all day.'

There was a desperate edge to my laughter. Rhonda and Richard were my sister- and brother-in-law. My siblings had both, inexplicably, persuaded good people to share their lives. It was the old story: I was the portable spinster whose role was to come home and be a sodding nursemaid.

I was too tired to argue. I'd fight my corner tomorrow.

'Let's see how we go,' I said.

THREE

Dad knocked on my door that evening, long after we'd said goodnight.

Sometime in the past twenty-five years, he'd slapped magnolia paint over the top of my bedroom wallpaper, covering the patches I'd ruined by sellotaping posters everywhere. Apart from that the room was pretty much unchanged from my childhood. Cobwebs still clung to the mellow rimu boards of the ceiling; here was my three-quarter-sized bed with the flowery quilt, my sheepskin rug, my bookcase—*All Creatures Great and Small*, *What Katy Did*, *The Hobbit*. Even my lava lamp.

Raewyn, bless her, had made the bed. I was sitting cross-legged on it, a towel around my wet hair, sending a message to Nathan. He was always a far better student than his mother. He graduated in psychology, and promptly set off to teach English in far-flung places. I missed him, but I couldn't complain. He had the travel bug, same as I did at his age. The downside? His girlfriend had tagged along. The dreaded Ella.

His reply was cheerful: *Hey Mum, good to know you got there in one piece! We're on a bus to the old port. Sleep well, love to Grandpa X*

The knock on my door was confident and brisk. Dad's voice was confident and brisk to match.

'Emily? You still awake?'

He stood in the corridor with a manila envelope in his hand. No confusion, no blankness. He looked a lot fitter than I felt. His eyes were still clear, his jawline firm, his complexion had the same fresh bloom as ever.

'Got everything you need?' he asked, glancing into the room behind me.

'Everything's great. Raewyn even put flowers by my bed.'

'Oh, good.' He held up the envelope. 'Something for you to look after.'

'What's this?'

'Keep it for me, will you? Please, please, don't open it until the event mentioned on the front. Until then, I'd rather you didn't let anyone know of its existence. I will undoubtedly forget I've given it to you. I'm afraid I'm going doolally.'

'No, Dad!'

'Oh, of course I am.' He waved away my denial. 'Don't be ridiculous. That's why you're here, isn't it? It's a bastard of a thing.'

'It might not be what they think.'

He placed the envelope in my hands.

'It *is* what they think. I know you mean to comfort me, but I'd rather not lie to myself. You'll keep this to yourself, and unopened? The contents could do a great deal of harm if they emerge too soon.'

'Sure, Dad. I promise. I'll guard it with my life.'

There's a child in all of us, and mine was flattered. My father was confiding in me! That was a first.

'A *great* deal of harm,' he repeated.

'Why don't you just burn it?'

'Because truth matters. History matters. Not alternative facts, not lies.' He nodded at the envelope. 'You'll know what to do with it, when the time comes.'

'What's in here?'

But the conversation was over. He thanked me and wished me a good night's sleep. I watched him stride off down the panelled corridor towards his own bedroom—hands in pockets, head high, as though he was back in his heyday.

I closed my door and examined the envelope in my hand. Its flap was stuck down with masking tape. On the front, Dad had written in blue-black ink—fountain pen, not a biro:

NOT TO BE OPENED UNTIL AFTER MY DEATH
After that, it's open season.
F.K.

Probably his will. Maybe he was leaving everything to his beloved Kauri hospice. Perhaps he'd bequeathed the Arapito land to Ira? That would make sense. Our hundred or so acres had been leased to the Parata family forever, and Ira did more for Dad than any of his own children. It would be hilarious to see the twins' faces when they found out.

An incorrigible devil on my shoulder suggested peeling back the masking tape and steaming open the envelope. Go on! I was a dab hand at letter-steaming; I routinely held Carmen's mail over the kettle when she was a teenager. Her love letters were hilarious. One outstanding effort, from a jug-eared lad called Zach, quoted Shakespeare. *Shall I compare thee to a summer's day?* When Carmen caught Ira and me in hysterics over it, she burst into tears and burned it in the fireplace in her room. I must have been such an annoying younger sister.

But I wasn't ten years old anymore. I slid Dad's envelope into my suitcase and climbed into bed. As I turned off the lamp, I made a mental note to thank Raewyn for making my room so welcoming. I owed her.

I'd forgotten the extreme remoteness of my old home. A plover screeched in the enormous darkness; a sheep coughed, hacking like the pack-a-day smoker I used to be. The house creaked as its wooden structure cooled down.

I was six when we left Leeds. I bade a snotty, tearful goodbye to my very, very best friend ever . . . what was her name? Poppy? Penny? Nope, it's gone . . . and we flew all the way across the world to this strange settlement, huddled under the mountains, where the shops shut all weekend, where children went to school barefoot and dogs were workers, not pets. Back then, the bright lights of Tawanui consisted of the milk bar and fish-and-chip shop.

At first we lived in a damp rental house in town, arranged by the Health Board, but my parents soon bought Arapito. Back in the late 1970s, both house and land seemed amazingly affordable.

'Space to breathe,' exulted Dad, the first time we all walked across the paddocks to the river, clutching our towels.

'Too much space,' said Mum. 'There's nothing here.'

'Can I have a horse?' asked Carmen.

'Hey, Emily,' said Eddie one night. 'D'you know the story of Arapito homestead?'

We were sitting beside the wood-burning stove in the snug. Mum was collecting Carmen from pony club. Dad, of course, was out at work. He was always at work. House calls, meetings, emergencies at the hospice.

'What story?' I asked, because I hadn't yet worked out that my brother was an idiot.

'Mr Izzard.'

'Who's Mr Izzard?'

Eddie shone a torch up from under his chin as he spun his tale. The eleven-year-old boy became a ghoul, with a glowing face and empty-skull eyes.

'Hilary Izzard,' he said, 'lived in this house years ago. His wife died of a fever on the passage over from England. In those days they used to throw the dead bodies overboard.'

I was open-mouthed. 'Why?'

'Because they didn't have fridges and things. They chucked Mrs Izzard into the sea and the sharks got her. Mr Izzard saw the water turn red, like tomato ketchup. He was really upset, but he came and lived here and farmed this land. And then his only son was killed in the First World War, and finally all his sheep died.'

'Why did they die?'

'A disease took them out. The whole flock. He was the unluckiest man in Tawanui. He went to town and paid all his bills. Then he came home and hanged himself in this very room. See that nail in the beam, right above your head? That's where he tied the rope. It was a week before they found him, and he was mostly maggots by then. They cut what was left of him down and took him away to be buried in the town cemetery. His grave's by the gate. Hilary Izzard.'

'I don't believe you,' I whimpered, wriggling away from underneath the nail in the beam.

Eddie dropped his voice to a guttural rasp. 'He never left this house. People hear his footsteps. People hear the rope, still swinging. That's how come we bought it so cheap.'

For years I lived in terror of that restless spirit. I'd seen Hilary Izzard's grave in the cemetery, and our old house never stopped breathing and shifting as it cooled and warmed. I used to hide under my flowery quilt, listening for footsteps in the corridor or the rhythmic creak of a rope as a decomposing body turned in the wind.

Eddie had made it all up, of course. Years later I did a school project on local history, interviewing men and women who were born in the nineteenth century. No Izzard had ever lived in our house. The Hilary Izzard in Tawanui cemetery was a grandmother-of-many, who died peacefully at the age of ninety.

As sleep began to swallow me, I heard Dad making his way to the bathroom. Steady, calm footsteps, not the ghost of a grieving farmer. It was a profoundly comforting sound. He was still my dad, after all.

•

Four in the bloody morning. Wide awake under a sheet, sweating, maddened by the whine of predatory mosquitoes. I'd forgotten how those little vampires could make a summer night a misery. My feet wouldn't keep still, my mind turned whooping somersaults.

The next moment I'd thrown off the sheet and was feeling my way down the porch steps, hobbling across the drought-stricken lawn, my toes curling upwards as prickle weed jabbed my soles. I could dimly make out Mum's croquet set on the porch, the white posts where we used to tie the tennis net, those spiky-headed cabbage trees in the paddock. I knew every shadow, every glint of the moonlight.

As a child I used to lie flat on my back on the trampoline on this lawn, blinking up at the blaze of the Milky Way with its dark holes and hazy patches of stardust. I clearly remember looking for God up there. One night, Dad came home late from a call-out to the hospice. He must have spotted me in his headlights as he drove up. I expected him to head straight inside, but he didn't. I heard the car door shut, his steady footfall approaching the trampoline.

'Stargazing?' he asked.

To my astonishment and delight, he swung easily up beside me and lay on his back, just as I was doing. As always, he kept a good foot or two of space between us. I've no memory of him ever properly hugging me, or any of his children—or his wife, come to think of it. The best he could manage was a fleeting arm around the shoulders. I've no memory of sitting on his knee, or holding his hand. He didn't do those things. He rarely touched people at all, unless they were his patients. But this night, he lay near me on the trampoline, both of us staring at the sky.

'Have you ever wondered what the name of our mountains means?' he asked. 'The Ruahine Range. *Rua-hine*. Wise woman. And they do seem wise somehow, don't they?'

'I feel as though they're watching me,' I said, and he said, yes, he felt that too. My dad understood me! I was euphoric.

He knew all about the night sky. He knew about so many things. His memory was astonishing. If he read something once, he remembered it. He pointed out the constellations and named the planets. He explained that in Māori legend, Orion's belt was a perch upon which birds would alight in order to eat the brilliant star, Rigel—though they called it Puanga—which, he told me, was as bright as forty thousand suns. 'See there? See how it could be a perch for a bird?'

Ever since then, I've thought of Dad when I look up at Orion's belt.

'And Betelgeuse,' he added, pointing. 'That's a red supergiant. It's used up all the hydrogen and it's burning stuff like carbon and helium now.'

I couldn't see which one he meant, but I pretended I could. I wanted this to go on forever, my father treating me like a proper person, showing me these things with exotic names. It was one of the very happiest moments of my life. It still is.

I desperately wanted to say something clever and worthy.

'And what's that one?' I asked, pointing. 'It's moving.'

'Um, that's a plane.'

I felt so stupid.

I wanted to tell him that looking at the universe made me feel like a feeble, flickering match that could be snuffed out at any moment. I wanted to tell him that I felt lonely and frightened when I lay here, and that was exactly why I did it. I wanted to ask him if it had the same effect on him, whether he ever felt lonely. But I was afraid he'd think me even more stupid, so I didn't say another word. Soon he got up, remarking that it was past my bedtime.

We never stargazed together again. But I took that moment, wrapped it in tissue paper and stored it away. I kept a few treasures like that: moments when I'd felt almost close to my father. From time to time over the years I would get them out and look at them.

The trampoline was long gone now. It had a good innings which finally ended when Nathan and his cousins—Carmen's kids—put their clod-hopping little feet right through the mat. Instead, I stretched out on the dry grass where it used to be, and watched Orion stalking across the sky.

In three weeks' time, this night would be just another memory. I'd be on my way back to London. Even if I saw Dad again, he wouldn't know me. And I would never have known him.

FOUR

The music of early morning in Arapito: that lyrical, liquid *quardle-ardle-wardle* of magpies in the garden. They sound mellow, but it's a different story altogether if they think their young are under threat. One time, Ira and I were playing on the woolshed roof when a black-and-white shadow dived in from nowhere, pecking and scolding as we scrambled to escape. Ira ended up with a bleeding cheek.

I was pulling a sundress over my head when Mum called on my mobile. How was my flight? she wanted to know. And how was I doing, and what was the state of play at Cold Comfort Farm?

'Flight fine,' I told her. 'I'm feeling better for a night's sleep. Cold Comfort Farm is basking in sunshine. How about you?'

I stood at the window, looking out at the cobwebs on her croquet set, listening while she talked. It hadn't stopped raining all bloody week in Yorkshire. The bloody train drivers were on strike. Malcolm was in the garage, polishing his already-immaculate Vauxhall Viva. I wondered whether she ever regretted swapping Dad for dull Malcolm. Probably not. Her second husband hung on her every word, was always telling her he loved her. Dad did neither.

'And Felix?' she asked. 'Is it true . . . Alzheimer's?'

She wanted all the details. *Is he eating? Is he depressed? What can I do to help? Would it cheer him up if I sent a calendar with lots of lovely Yorkshire scenes?* She talked about her ex an awful lot for someone who pretended not to care at all. When I mentioned that Raewyn wanted me to stay on, her volume increased by several decibels. At times like this she sounded very like Carmen, except with Yorkshire vowels and smoker's throatiness.

'Emmy! Get out of there, for Christ's sake—get out, while you still can.'

'I intend to.'

'He's asking too much of you. Don't let him make you feel guilty.'

I tried to explain that Dad wasn't asking for anything at all. This had her snorting.

'Ooh, don't you believe it. He asks too much of everyone. He asked me to leave my whole life behind and emigrate! That was his dream, but it certainly wasn't mine. To be fair, he asks too much of himself as well. It's all down to his super-religious upbringing.'

'He's an atheist.'

'Bollocks. He wants to be. He *tries* to be. But I knew his parents. Bloody awful people, especially Nan Kirkland. Mother and Father, he called them—not Mum and Dad, Mother and Father! Isn't that creepy? Two bags of frozen peas would be warmer than that pair of horrors. They were hung up on sex. Mary Whitehouse was their heroine.'

'Who?'

'Google her. They were the sort of Christians who'd make Christ weep. They raised Felix and poor little Helen to believe Jesus was reading their minds like some kind of supernatural KGB agent, ready to pounce if they so much as thought the word "knickers". Guilt, guilt, guilt. No amount of critical thinking can free you from that kind of guilt, not when it's instilled in you from your mother's knee.'

I had a dim memory of a visit Nan and Grandpa *almost* made to Tawanui. Mum cleaned and gardened for weeks before their arrival, threatening dire consequences for us children if we swore, squabbled or disgraced her in any way. She kept yelling at my father for inviting the bloody people in the first place, to which he replied wretchedly that they'd invited themselves.

Fate intervened. Hours before the dreaded visitors were due to set out, we heard that Nan had collapsed with a heart attack and died in Leeds General. We were all very relieved. Mum said we'd dodged a bullet.

'What's the solution for Dad, though?' I asked now.

A flick of her lighter, a long moment's hesitation as she inhaled. When she spoke again, she sounded pensive. 'I was right to leave him. You know I had to, don't you? We married in haste, couple of kids, repented at leisure. You only get one life and I couldn't stay in Tawanui for the rest of mine.'

'Nobody blames you, Mum.'

'I don't want you to end up like me, depressed and desperate.'

Credit to my mother. She was miserably homesick here, but she stuck it out until her last child had flown the nest—that was me, heading off to university. Then she handed Dad an ultimatum. She'd done her bit, she said, and now she was going home. Was he coming, or wasn't he?

A month later she was on her way. Alone. The next time we heard from her she was back in Yorkshire with her four sisters.

'At one time I wondered'—I imagined her tapping her ash into a pot plant—'whether he might be having an affair.'

'With?'

'Raewyn.'

'Raewyn!' That had me giggling.

'He was a very attractive man.' Mum sounded defensive.

'She's hardly a vampish siren. She's cuddly. Like a hobbit.'

'Cuddly at seventy-odd, a voluptuous redhead at forty. Felix admired her for driving that bus full of kids, being superhuman through Manu's illness. She could back trailers up steep tracks, crutch sheep, build fences . . .'

I was sure there wasn't a smidgeon of sexual chemistry between Raewyn and Dad. She was a one-man woman, and that man was Manu. As for Dad, he was far too uptight to play the away game. I'd never even seen him flirt with a woman. He used to tut disapprovingly at fictional infidelity on soap operas.

'I wish they *were* secret lovers,' I said. 'I'd feel better about her doing so much for him now. But it's a ludicrous suggestion, Mum, and you know it.'

At that moment the man himself knocked on my bedroom door, asking if I wanted a cup of coffee because he'd just made a pot. I called out that I'd be right along, and heard his footsteps heading for the kitchen.

'That was him, wasn't it?' Mum's tone had softened. 'Oh, bugger. I'd forgotten. He sounds so courteous, doesn't he? Such a gentleman.'

'I'd better go.'

'Please tell him . . . I don't know. Just tell him hello from me.'

•

I arrived in the kitchen to find the sliding glass door wide open, curtains stirring in a faint breeze. The mountains had begun to shimmer.

I stepped onto the porch for a moment, inhaling the sweetness of the morning air. Gloria was already settled into her daytime sleeping position in the shade, but I could hear Gyp somewhere under the house, making a hell of a racket. I knew from my last visit home that he liked to think of himself as an excellent ratter—which was delusional, because he never caught anything.

He could smell rats through the wooden floorboards; he'd waddle around the house, nose pressed to the ground, sniffing, yapping, scratching. Sometimes—like now—his tail would disappear into the dark spaces between the piles, and we'd hear crazed barking.

'They're laughing at you, Gyp,' I called to him. 'Give it up, man. Live and let live.'

Dad was proudly filling our mugs from the coffee pot, pouring slowly but with precision despite his shaking hands. I thanked him, and he didn't notice me sidling over to turn off the gas ring. He gestured at the table, where several cardboard boxes were overflowing with what looked like rubbish.

'This is the kind of thing,' he said. 'You see? I used to keep everything filed but I can't seem to manage anymore. Rather disheartening.'

I took a look. Dad never threw away a power bill, bank statement or letter from a friend. Everything used to be scrupulously filed and organised, but there was nothing ordered about the contents of these boxes. Magazines and pamphlets, catalogues and leaflets, takeaway menus and unopened copies of *The Watchtower*. Bills and letters and reports and . . .

'Let's get started, then,' I suggested briskly. 'I bet most of this can be chucked out.'

I found more cardboard boxes in the pantry, which I explained were for 'fire-lighting', 'recycling' and 'to be filed'. Dad sat impassively, watching my flurry of activity. I began by picking up a fundraising letter from Greenpeace.

'Recycling?'

He frowned at it. 'But they do such good work.'

'They do, but you don't have to keep all their letters.'

'I haven't read it yet.'

'Okay.' *Pick your battles*. I dropped that one into the *To be filed* box. Next up was a circular about a treatment for migraines.

'Definitely recycling,' I said.

'Let me see?'

He laid it on the table, feeling for his glasses in his top pocket. At this rate, it was going to take centuries to get the job done.

'You know, Dad, we could just leave all this,' I suggested. 'It isn't doing any harm.'

'These people are despicable charlatans,' he announced, whipping off his glasses. 'This drug has been withdrawn. Nasty side effects. I'd never prescribe it.'

'Oh good! Shall we bin it?'

'No, I think I'd better hold on to this.'

I tried one last time, lifting out an overflowing file marked *Kauri hospice*. Dad hadn't been in New Zealand five minutes before word was out that he had a special interest in palliative care—and five minutes after that, he was on the board of the local hospice. Mum was hopping mad. *He's never at home as it is. What about his own family?*

'Surely this can go?' I begged. 'You've retired.'

'I can't just throw a whole file away!'

I sighed. It was going to be a long day.

•

I soon gave up on the job. Dad wouldn't let me bin anything, so I left him to it. I made more coffee and read a *National Geographic* article about the rapidly thawing permafrost in Siberia. It was an ecological catastrophe, but there was one fascinating aspect: all kinds of prehistoric beasts were emerging from the ice, most recently a young woolly mammoth that had lain frozen for forty thousand years. I was enchanted by a photograph of this creature, perfectly preserved and oddly beautiful, surrounded by reverential scientists. You could tell it was a baby. It might only be asleep.

'Look,' I said, holding up the article. 'The ice is giving up its secrets.'

No reply from Dad. He hadn't spoken for ten minutes. His face seemed to be melting, the bags under his eyes dragging downwards.

'I think I might pack up for now,' he mumbled. 'Shall we carry all this back?'

The study was his sacred domain; we children rarely set foot in there. He'd always been pedantic about keeping it tidy, everything in its place. I grabbed what I could, followed him down the corridor—and stopped dead in the doorway.

I was looking into a dragon's cave, but instead of glittering treasure, every surface was covered in paper and dust. I couldn't even see the green leather top of the desk. The most chilling sight was something terribly mundane: a grey Fair Isle jersey and scarf draped over the back of the desk chair. I remembered these all too well, because Dad lent them to Nathan that last time we visited. Just before we left, Nathan laid the folded jersey and scarf over that chair. I saw him do it. And they were still there, exactly as Nathan had left them. *Exactly.* They hadn't moved an inch. They smelled musty. Three years.

Dad wandered out, and I heard the bolt of the bathroom door. I took the opportunity to peek into his desk drawers. I expected more chaos, but I was wrong. Complete precision. Dr Kirkland's meticulous organisation, preserved in amber: address book, stamps, stapler, calculator. Yellowed envelopes, USB sticks, printer ink. The whole study was like Dad's mind: cluttered, confused, with a wealth of history and pockets of antiquated order.

In the centre drawer I found a bundle of diaries, held together with a rubber band. A photograph was tucked among them, one of a batch taken by Carmen's husband-to-be in the days leading up to their wedding. This one showed us three adult children playing croquet with Mum. She travelled from England for the Big Day—her first and only return to Tawanui. My parents declared a truce, and she threw herself into the plans: making table decorations, bossing the vicar, ordering more flowers and wine. She loved a party, and this was one hell of a bash—a sumptuous, winter wedding in Tawanui church, with a reception at the Tawa Hills vineyard. It was also the last time my family were all together.

Dad had written our names on the back of the picture, along with the date: 9th June 1994. It summed us all up: Mum, undisputed croquet champion and completely merciless, aiming her mallet at the black ball. Carmen and I were laughing, trying to push each other over. Eddie stood to one side with his arms crossed. Dad wasn't there.

Picking up the most recent diary—2016—I flicked through its pages. I didn't feel I was violating Dad's privacy. This was an appointment diary, not a pour-out-your-heart-and-soul one. Routine entries. *Kauri board meeting 7 pm. Gloria to vet 9 am. Carmen's birthday*.

I turned to January, looking for the day Nathan and I flew in.

Emily (DAUGHTER) and grandson NATHAN arrive TODAY
Meet them at Hawke's Bay airport 10.40 am
9 AM I MUST LEAVE HERE TO PICK THEM UP
They live in LONDON. Emily illustrates books (ARTIST)
Nathan has left school? Going to university? (CHECK!)

The entries weren't as spidery as the writing on the labels around the house, but still not right—as though they'd been written carefully, painfully, by someone whose hand wasn't quite obeying the commands of their brain.

Nathan and I spent over a fortnight in this house. Why did neither of us notice the state the poor man was in? Or perhaps I did notice. Perhaps I refused to acknowledge it to myself. *There's none so blind*, my mother used to say, *as them that won't see*. What a useless daughter.

Towards the back of the diary, I found a section for notes. This, too, was covered in writing. I skim-read, keeping a guilty ear out for Dad's return.

WAYMARKS
I am FELIX GERALD KIRKLAND
3 children CARMEN, EDWARD, EMILY
6 grandchildren: Esme, Natalie (Eddie's), Nicholas, Shona, Oliver (Carmen's), Nathan (Emily's)
I was born in LEEDS. I went to Leeds Grammar School. I was tennis captain
Our family dog was SHEP, my best friend was Alan Trentham
I studied medicine at Merton College, Oxford
MY PARENTS are SUSAN AND GERALD KIRKLAND
My sister HELEN died aged 18
EX wife Lillian. Amicable divorce?
I am a doctor (GP). I was partner in the health centre in Tawanui
I AM A DOCTOR—remember this
LEAH
LEAH LEAH
REMEMBER!

Dad's voice made me leap like a startled rabbit. I hadn't heard the bathroom door, nor his footsteps.

'Bit of a mess in here, I'm afraid,' he said sadly.

'Looking for a stamp,' I lied, shutting the drawers. 'I've found them. Thanks.'

'I really need to tackle all this.'

'None of it matters, Dad.'

He protested that it *did* matter, and we agreed to keep working on it another day. I left him in his armchair, the only uncluttered space in the study. I was sure he'd be asleep within minutes.

Back in my room, I slid my suitcase from under the bed and fished out the brown envelope. *NOT TO BE OPENED UNTIL AFTER MY DEATH*. The handwriting matched the wobbly letters in Dad's three-year-old diary. I imagined him sitting at his desk, sensing the gathering mist and desperately trying to leave waymarks for himself. He'd listed the things that most mattered to him, the treasures of seventy-plus years of life condensed into a few lines of quavering handwriting. He must have been terrified.

There was something else, though. Unsettling, confusing.

He'd named the most important people in his life. Off the top of my head, I could count at least five others I might have expected him to mention: Raewyn, of course, and what about Ira and Manu? His colleague Dr Marcia Ellis, volunteer search and rescue friends like Dave Perry. Not one of these people had been chosen as waymarks.

So why—why on *earth*—had he written Leah Parata's name three times?

FIVE

June 1994

I envy you, she says, and buys her chocolate, and drives away into the rain. She hasn't a care in the world. Everyone thinks they have a tomorrow.

It's a Friday. As soon as my shift ends, I rush home to change. I'm off to the cinema to see *Jurassic Park* with a friend called Greta Miller and some others. I've persuaded Ira to join us. He brings along a guy I knew slightly at school, a blond forestry worker called Brad Taylor.

Tawanui cinema is always good for a laugh. It's run by a smiley woman who sells tickets, drinks and popcorn from a booth before taking back those same tickets two minutes later at the door to the auditorium. Once her audience is sitting down, she opens the curtains and starts the film.

By the time the survivors of Jurassic Park have flown into the sunset, and we all spill onto the street, the rain is taking a breather. The stars are out. Nobody wants to break up the party, so we pick up supplies from the bottle store and head for Brad Taylor's place. He's the huntin' and shootin' type—owns a camo jacket, more than one rifle and a Hilux with off-road tyres. He shows me a wild pig in his freezer, which he's butchered himself. I've never been into that brand of machismo, but I'm young and drunk. I'm also demob happy, because after months of saving up I've just bought a one-way ticket to London via South America.

Six of us huddle under blankets on the deck, all ex-pupils from Tawanui High. Brad and I share the oily car seat he uses as a sofa. Ira sinks deep into a beanbag, puffing clouds of Brad's home-grown cannabis. I come back from a trip to the bathroom to hear people arguing in the slow-motion drawl of the hopelessly stoned.

'It's saving my sister's snails,' Ira's saying. 'Saving the kiwi and the whio and the tuatara and . . . um, saving the planet, saving—'

Brad interrupts him. 'Not saving anything—it's cruel shit! They're just dropping poison from the sky, great clouds of it. Poisoning the water and everything.'

I'm sober enough to guess what the cruel shit is: a pest-control poison called 1080, pronounced ten-eighty, designed to kill imported predators. Aerial drops have been going on for decades in New Zealand's wilderness areas. People have been arguing bitterly about it forever.

'Poisoned my dog,' says Brad. 'She died in agony, spewing green stuff.'

Ira's shaking his head. 'I know she did, mate. But you've got no reason to think that was 1080.'

'Your sister's in the pockets of those fucking chemical companies. What are they paying her? Huh? I heard her on the radio, saying it's a necessary evil. She always gets wheeled out to defend it. I bet they're paying her to lie for them.'

Ira's brows draw together. He's staunchly loyal to Leah. If he and Brad hadn't smoked quite so much wacky baccy, the argument might have turned nasty, but it just meanders back and forth, nobody making much sense.

'Bullshit,' Ira murmurs, passing the spliff along to Greta and her boyfriend Marty, who are sharing a hammock. 'All she cares about is saving what's left of our native creatures. She's up at Biddulph's right now, just so—'

'So she and her mates can poison everything that moves, so I can't hunt for my own food.'

'If we don't control the predators, we can say goodbye to our native birds 'cos they'll all be extinct. Silent forests. Is that what you want, mate? Silent forests?'

At that moment Marty falls right out of the hammock, which sets off shrieks of laughter and mockery. The 1080 spat is forgotten. Someone puts on Dire Straits' *Telegraph Road*. Eventually the conversation turns to gossip about Eddie.

'Getting all handsy with Leah during that slow dance,' scoffs Greta, who was at Carmen's wedding last Saturday. 'You'd think he'd have got the message by now.'

'Fiftieth time lucky,' I say.

'I thought she was going to slap his face.'

'He's got that kind of face,' says Brad. 'You want to slap it.'

I don't even try to stand up for my brother. I'm suffering from the distorting effect of far too much Steinlager, which lends Brad a kind of Nordic warrior appeal.

One thing leads to another. It's not my finest hour.

•

I wake up under grubby sheets, with a thundering hangover and Brad's elbow in my face. He doesn't seem remotely like a Nordic warrior this morning, more of a Big Mistake. What was I *thinking?* I grab my scattered clothes and creep out of the house, vowing to steer well clear of Brad Taylor until I leave the country. I'm sure he'll feel the same when he wakes up.

It's pouring again. I start my car, turn on the wipers, blink through the headache. Due at work at eight. That's in—squinting at my watch, struggling to focus—*Oh God, no!* Twenty-five minutes.

I drive like the clappers. Make it. Just. Get the petrol station open, put out the signs and spend my day filling people's cars in the rain. At about lunchtime Eddie's Mini turns onto the forecourt, and he leaps out. He's been home for Carmen's wedding but is heading back to Auckland today. I wave through the window; he doesn't wave back.

'Brad Taylor?' he rages, barging into the shop. 'Brad fucking *Taylor*? Of all the useless pricks, you have to choose that cretin?'

'He spoke very highly of you.'

'Jesus Christ! I can't come home for a week without some smug twat telling me he's just shagged my sister.'

'Wasn't very gentlemanly of him to tell you, was it?'

'You've got no shame, Emily! You're just a massive embarrassment. Brad *Taylor*?'

He plants himself in front of the counter—just where Leah stood yesterday—raging about how much he despises everything about Tawanui: the place is a fucking cesspit full of small-minded morons with nothing better to do than gossip, and his own sister is the town bike.

That's going too far. I know precisely where his skin is thinnest, and I stick the knife right in.

'Not hard to guess what's made you so bitter,' I say with a nasty smirk. 'You tried to get off with Leah at Carmen's wedding—yes, you did. Everyone saw you draping yourself over her, everyone knows. You made a fool of yourself. I bet Brad was winding you up about it.'

I've hit the mark. The words are barely out of my mouth before he's grabbed the sunglasses display stand and is hurling it across the floor. I yell at him, he yells at me, and he's about to push over another stand when a parade of motorcyclists rumbles onto the forecourt, parking their bikes and removing their helmets:

five burly men in serious biking leathers. They're heading straight into the shop.

Eddie knows when he's beaten. Seconds later there's rubber coming off his tyres as he heads north on his way to Auckland. The motorcycling saviours find me trying to clear up the mess. They lift up the stand, and even replace all the sunglasses for me. One of them, a bearded giant, says he's got a daughter my age. *Twenty-one! Best age to be.*

'That was your brother?' he asks, jabbing a thumb towards the road. 'What's wrong with him?'

'I think he needs help with his anger management.'

'Huh! I'd like to give him anger management.'

•

I arrive home to find Mum playing her piano in the parlour. Poor Dad has gone down with this winter's vicious flu bug. He's flat out in bed with his curtains drawn and his eyes shut, refusing all offers of drinks or food.

'Eddie's gone,' says Mum. 'It was awful having to say goodbye to him. He was upset. I wish you'd all come and live near me.'

I've already decided not to mention the drama of Eddie's visit to the petrol station. I don't feel like confessing to that one-night stand with Brad Taylor.

Mum and I spend most of the weekend playing cards in the snug. It's lovely to have her to myself. We make mulled wine and plan all the things we'll do together when my travels finally take me to Britain. Dad doesn't appear at all, though we hear him throwing up in the bathroom.

'Poor Felix.' Mum can't quite hide her glee. 'But what do you expect, when you spend every waking moment in a consulting room with people coughing and sneezing all over you?'

It's a good thing Carmen didn't choose this weekend for her wedding, because it would have been a wash out. If you didn't know the Ruahines were there, you wouldn't know they were there. Low cloud covers them like a magician's silk cloth. Sometimes the cloth is briefly whisked away—*ta-dah!*—to reveal bleak uplands and steep faces. I stand at the kitchen window and imagine Leah in her waterproof jacket with her hood up, slipping and sliding through the dripping underbrush.

'All that fuss over a flesh-eating snail,' I say.

'When's she due back? Monday?' Mum pretends to shiver. 'I bet Raewyn will have the home fires burning and all kinds of goodies baking in the oven.'

Raewyn phones on Tuesday morning. I'll never forget it.

•

Dad answers. He's up and dressed, though I don't think he's over his flu. I hear Raewyn's voice down the line, and immediately his gaze turns towards the ranges.

'Where was she headed?' he asks. 'When exactly did she say she'd be back?' He runs his hand across his face, pinches his nose, says he'll organise everything. 'Try not to worry, Raewyn.'

'Leah?' I ask, as he hangs up.

He nods tersely, already making the first of three rapid calls: the police, the regional search and rescue coordinator, the health centre.

Carmen wanders in during the last of these, wearing a fluffy dressing-gown. She and Richard have stopped for a night on their way back from their honeymoon. In a whisper, I explain what's up.

'We'll be able to get a locum,' says Dad down the phone. 'Look, I am not, repeat *not*, coming in. What? No, I don't know how long.'

Minutes later he's changed into hiking clothes and is rummaging in the boot room. He emerges with an armful of gear: ropes, a first-aid kit, a torch, a flare.

'It's okay, isn't it?' asks Carmen. 'She's hardly even late. Probably just needed a bit longer for her research.'

Dad's whole body seems taut.

'She's not some airheaded tourist,' he snaps, shrugging into his jacket. 'She'd know people would start looking for her. Ira's been up to the trail head and found her car. This weather . . .' He looks out of the window. 'Not good.'

'But you've had the flu, Dad,' I protest. 'You're in no fit state.'

He ignores me. He has one foot up on a kitchen chair, lacing his boots.

'She was planning to spend the night in Biddulph's on Friday,' I tell him, desperate to be helpful. 'Then head across the saddle. She stopped at the petrol station on her way.'

That gets his attention. He glances up at me, still tying a lace. 'You saw her? When?'

'Er . . . Friday morning.'

'Right.' He grabs his cap. 'I'm going to collect Ira. We're heading up to Biddulph's, in case there's any sign of her there. She could be injured.'

'I'd like to help,' says Carmen to his departing back, 'but I've got work—'

He's already gone. His engine revs, wheels churning mud as he tears off towards the road gate.

I don't think the newlyweds are enjoying the fact that their honeymoon has ended in someone else's crisis. They load a mountain of wedding presents into the boot of their car, trotting out lies about how Leah will be in their prayers. They both kiss Mum goodbye and promise to visit her next year in the UK. They're gone within half an hour.

And then the awful waiting begins.

•

Mum and I keep Raewyn company. Dad has persuaded her to stay put in case Leah turns up or phones. We make cups of tea and try to say hopeful things.

'Leah knows what she's doing,' ventures Mum.

'As well as anyone else alive,' agrees Raewyn, with a staunch compression of her lips. I've seen that look before, when the school bus got stuck in the mud and she had all us kids out and pushing. 'Manu taught her and Ira what to do if they were ever lost. She took her very first steps up there. Whatever's happened, she'll survive.'

She tilts her head at the rumble of the cattle grid. 'Who is it?' she cries, jumping up and rushing outside. 'Please, God, let it be her!'

But it's only Dad and Ira.

'We found her log,' says Ira, holding up a piece of paper covered in Leah's handwriting.

Most back-country huts are equipped with a logbook. Hikers record details of their intended route, the conditions, anything noteworthy. Biddulph's bivvy is meant to have one too, but it seems to have been lost. Perhaps the book had been used to light a fire, or gnawed by rats and thrown away. It doesn't matter, because Leah—a meticulous record keeper—has detailed her plans on a torn-out page of her own research notebook, even leaving a blank page for future visitors to use. Ira and Dad found her note on the packing-case table, weighed down with an old beer bottle that served as a candlestick. It's written in blue biro. Leah gives the time and date—*7.30 am, Saturday 18/6/94*—and reports that she's just spent one night in the hut. She mentions that rats are living under the floor and offers to bring poison on her next visit. She describes the weather: *heavy showers, strong gusts, poor visibility.* She explains that her goal is to establish suitable monitoring sites for the next phase of a study into the effects of aerial drops of 1080 on populations of *Powelliphanta marchanti*. She has two remote areas to survey, and she intends to bivouac in them for the next two nights. She plans to pass by Biddulph's again on her way out. She says she'll update the log then.

But she never did.

SIX

February 2019

'But you don't *need* to go shopping.' Dad sounded agitated. 'There's a kitchen full of food.'

I had my back to him, searching for bags in the pantry.

'Just one or two things. Come with me? We're bound to bump into people you know.'

That much was true. A stroll down the main street of Tawanui had always been a social occasion for Dad, whether he liked it or not. Everyone knew him. I thought it might do him good, and I was keen to have a change of scene. I'd been home for a day and was already feeling claustrophobic.

I should have guessed what he'd do next. Stupid of me.

'Okay,' he sighed. 'I'll drive you.'

I swore under my breath. Now what? I wasn't equipped for tiptoeing across this minefield. I'd scarcely known my father when he was at the top of his game, let alone now that he was turning into someone else.

He was looking at the hook where he used to keep his car keys.

'Can't find my keys.'

'You aren't allowed to drive, Dad.'

He turned to stare at me, his mouth hanging open. 'Not allowed to drive? Who says I'm not allowed to drive?'

'People thought you might be better to stay off the roads for a while—you know, after you had that accident. And you agreed; you've given your car keys to Raewyn.'

His eyes snapped with rage. 'Don't talk such rubbish. Who are these people? How dare they?' He thumped his fist down onto the kitchen bench, making the crockery jump.

'It's not my fault,' I protested, taking several rapid steps backwards. 'I wasn't even here.'

He looked startled for a moment, and then confused, and the anger drained away. He rubbed his face with both hands, massaging the skin around his eyes. I wanted to give him a hug. Instead I barged about, pretending none of it had happened. I could have wept for him. The mighty were fallen so very, very far.

'I wish I could be up there,' he said. 'Could we go today?'

He was gazing at the ranges. Sunlight danced enticingly on the uplands.

'Not today, Dad.'

'Tomorrow?'

'Maybe.'

He sighed, gave a little shrug. As he turned away from the window, he noticed the shopping bags in my hand.

'Going somewhere?'

'Into Tawanui. Just a few errands.'

'Can you manage if I don't come with you? Do you know the way? I'm not sure whether you've been here before.'

'I know the way, Dad. Thanks.'

'I've got some letters to write.'

Ah, those mythical letters again. I said I would leave him to work in peace, and left him to them. Truth becomes dispensable when a person is being deleted.

•

Blink, and you'd miss Tawanui. Most people did, shooting past the turn-off as they sped along the main road. The town's resident population was only about four thousand, though that number was deceptive because it served an enormous rural area. You wouldn't find photos of the wide main street on your Glorious Landscapes of New Zealand calendar, and nobody ever filmed a blockbuster Tolkien trilogy there, yet whenever I came back, I was struck by the sheer splendour of its setting: on the edge of the Tukituki plains, as the land begins to swell into the Ruahine Range.

My first stop was the library, a breezeblock building opposite the picturesque little Anglican church. Mum used to work here, and sometimes I'd walk over after school and wait for her. Now I wandered among the shelves, hearing echoes of childhood: the rumble of ceiling fans, the clank of the trolley; the snuffles of that bald man who sat turning the pages of newspapers. I spent a while browsing in the section on dementia before choosing a book called *Stranger in My Mirror: A guide to Alzheimer's and dementia care*. The introduction described a patient who didn't recognise herself in the mirror. She was terrified out of her wits by the sinister intruder who was always there, staring into her eyes.

Don't try to argue, advised the author. *The emotion is real, even if the threat is not. Acknowledge her feelings, no matter how irrational. Show her that you understand. Above all, everyone longs to be understood.*

The librarian pottered about in a floral smock. I couldn't for the life of me remember her name, but she knew me. She worked here with Mum, back in the day.

'Your dad all right?' she asked, when I handed over his library card. 'Haven't seen him lately.'

'Keeping busy.'

'Dr Kirkland saved my life. Appendicitis, ouch!' She winced at the memory. 'Never known pain like it. If it weren't for him, I wouldn't be here now. And my nephew's baby, he was coughing . . .'

Nod and smile, nod and smile.

'I could never understand why Lillian left,' she whispered. 'I don't think she knew how lucky she was.'

Next stop was the supermarket. I was accosted again, this time by a bird-thin figure in a green nurse's uniform. Short hair, rimless glasses. Pamela had been the practice nurse at the Tawanui Health Centre forever.

'How's he doing?' she asked, as our trolleys blocked the produce aisle.

'So-so.'

'He still comes in now and again. He likes to write prescriptions—that's dead against the rules!—so I gave him a fake prescription pad. Keeps him happy.'

I was horrified. My father used to be like God in that surgery, and now his ex-colleagues were giving him pretend-doctor toys. What next? A plastic stethoscope?

'I'm sorry,' I said.

'Happy to make time for him. Felix had time for everyone, didn't he?'

Not for his family, I thought, but I nodded and smiled, nodded and smiled.

Heat and glare seared me as I stepped outside. I'd just finished lobbing my bags onto the back seat of my car when a flatbed truck came rumbling and creaking into the car park from the main street, giving an amiable little double-honk of salute. I felt a lift of delight as Ira hopped out: a spare, muscular figure in shorts and leather boots, the same quiet smile as his father. Tangled curls, almost shoulder-length. His right arm was heavily tattooed with a geometric design—he got that a couple of years after Leah vanished. I never asked, but I think it was a tribute to her, and perhaps to Manu also.

'Mum told me you'd fetched up,' he said.

By his standards this was a wildly effusive greeting, practically flirtatious.

'Yup,' I said. 'Large as life.'

'Twice as ugly.'

I told him that was the pot calling the kettle black, and he answered with a lift of his eyebrows. And then, silence. I scratched a mosquito bite on my arm; Ira scuffed the tarmac with the heel of his boot. I wasn't bothered. This was much what I expected. He wasn't great at small talk. Not anymore.

He was once the clown of the school bus, the boy who never stopped talking, never stopped laughing and singing and doing handstands, wasn't scared of anyone or anything. He was better than me at every single subject except art. Above all he was a sportsman: played rugby like a dervish and wanted to go professional. He ran the cross-country barefoot, always romping in a full minute ahead of everyone else. At ten, he was leader of the kapa haka group: strutting up and down the ranks of children, ramrod straight, yelling magnificently in te reo Māori. The hair stood up on the backs of my arms as he urged his warriors to show their strength and passion. I felt a thrill of pride in my friend, and in my adopted country.

But that was a long, long time ago. Ira's family descended into nightmare; his precious youth and talent were poured into running the farm. For him there was no professional rugby, no tertiary education, no travel. He lost his father at nineteen, his sister only two years later. The last time I saw him lead a haka was at her memorial service. He'd worn a look of wary resignation ever since, a man waiting for the next blow.

'Sorry your old man's not great,' he said now, as we stood on the melting tarmac.

'Was it you who stacked all that firewood on his porch?'

He shrugged. Ira never wanted to be thanked. He helped

Dad—and lots of others, I was sure—because it was what he did. He had a code of honour.

'You should come up for a beer,' he suggested. 'Tomorrow?'

•

The car was a stifling oven. I opened the windows as I headed out of town—past the saleyards, the timber mill and farm supply stores. Mirages gleamed in the undulations as the road began to gain altitude. I passed the rest area, with its giant sign: *You Are Now Standing on the Fortieth Parallel South*. When we were children, we used to get out here and stand with our feet on each side of the imaginary line. Dad liked to quote an old whalers' saying: *Beyond forty degrees south, there is no law. Beyond fifty, there is no God.*

I was still thinking about the whalers when I passed the Arapito turn-off to my left. I kept going—I was low on fuel, and now seemed a good time to fill up.

The petrol station hadn't changed much since my day, though the shop was better stocked, with a blue-and-white freezer for party ice out the front. It was manned by a young man with a ponytail and a brave attempt at a goatee.

'I used to work here,' I told him, as I tapped my card on the payWave machine. 'In 1994. Trip down memory lane for me.'

'I wasn't even born.'

'Well, I'm very old.'

He grinned. He looked nothing like Nathan, but he reminded me of Nathan all the same.

'I bet you're going to say it feels like yesterday,' he said.

As he printed my receipt, I found myself staring out through the plate-glass windows. The mountains were awash with sunshine. Butter wouldn't melt in their mouths. You'd never believe they could kill.

Right here, I thought. She was standing *right here*, where I was now, holding up her chocolate, twirling her turquoise beanie on her finger, chatting about Ecuador and giant snails. *Feels like yesterday.*

•

I didn't head straight home. On impulse, I turned north out of the petrol station, just as Leah did. I headed for Biddulph Road, as she did. It wasn't far. I was pulling onto the dusty verge when my phone rang. *Carmen*, said the caller ID.

'Sis!' I cried.

I could hear her nagging someone in the background. *No, no . . . you've missed the red flags. Have you looked at the notes? Well, look again.*

I tapped my fingernails on the steering wheel as I waited. She was playing a game, proving how busy and important she was. People who grow up together know each other so well, that's the trouble. There's nowhere to hide foibles, self-deceptions and total inanities. I've no doubt Carmen's customers saw a competent optometrist and businesswoman. I saw the teenager who had door-slamming meltdowns when Mum wouldn't take a day off work to drive her to a gymkhana, who turned a blind eye when Eddie practically threw me out of a tree. God knows what she saw when she looked at me.

'Emily?' she said at last. 'Hi! Sorry. Frantically busy here.'

'I can hear that.'

'Multi-tasking. Welcome to my world. Where are you?'

'In a very hot car, full of groceries. Welcome to my world.'

Instantly, she was irritated. 'Didn't you use the cool bags? I left some in the pantry. God, Dad is hopeless nowadays!'

I made the mistake of asking how she was, and she told me: paperwork backlog, a son off school with a sore throat, a horse with knee problems.

'And Dad,' she said. 'I'm so worried. He's not coping, is he?'

'I'm not sure.'

'St Patrick's have him on their waiting list. It's a question of dead man's boots. Or, rather, dead man's bed.'

'Did he agree to this?'

'No.' A sigh. 'But what else can we do? He's too far away for Eddie or me to keep an eye on him. He's not getting proper nutrition, he's losing weight. What's going to happen when he falls down the porch steps?'

'He's perfectly fit, physically.'

'I'm concerned about the influence Raewyn has over him. She cleans, she shops, she cooks. She's made herself indispensable. You have to wonder what she's getting out of it. Or *hoping* to get out of it, in his will. For Ira.'

There it was. Money.

'Now you're being absurd,' I said. 'Raewyn, a gold-digger?'

'Dad earned year after year, built up the practice, invested wisely. He's got shares, he's got a whopping private pension. He owns Arapito outright. Fifty-plus hectares of drought-safe country! Eddie asked a valuer, and the land alone is worth over a million dollars. What if he feels so grateful to the Paratas that he leaves his entire estate to them?'

'That's his choice.'

She was haranguing the luckless trainee again. *He's sixty, his parents both had glaucoma and he's experiencing migraines. How would you follow that up?*

'We need to respect Dad's intellect,' I said, once she was back. 'Obviously.'

'He isn't a child.'

Her voice changed up a gear. Carmen hates it when anyone questions her worldview.

'Do you think you've got a monopoly on insight, Emily? D'you think you're the only one who finds this difficult? I don't see *you* putting up your hand to have him live with you. I'm juggling about ten balls here, and you come swanning in for five minutes—'

The worst thing about a mobile phone is that you can't slam it down. It's not half so satisfying to press the *end call* icon. But I pressed it anyway, cutting her off in mid-yelp. Then I prowled around the car in the harsh light, cursing myself for throwing away the moral high ground. Why did I always do that? I'd been doing it since we were children. Well, I wasn't going to call back and apologise. Never had. Bloody well wasn't going to start now.

As the minutes passed, the countryside calmed me. The click and fizz of cicadas, the bellows of young bulls in a paddock beside the road, white butterflies flickering in the overgrown verges. From here, the ranges looked like sleeping giants, their jagged contours blurred by heat and dust.

Biddulph Road wasn't a road in any normal sense of the word; more a bone-jarringly corrugated and potholed track, leading to Almost Nowhere. There were several such unsealed access tracks along the Ruahine Range, each winding inwards and upwards, crossing streams on rattling wooden bridges. Even the most used were poorly maintained, and Biddulph had never been one of those. Best in a four-wheel drive.

A green Department of Conservation sign proclaimed that the Ruahine Forest Park lay twelve kilometres up the track. Someone had defaced it by spraying red letters from one side to the other. Dripping, livid. I'd seen graffiti like this before. I reached out, running my fingers along the crimson rage, remembering a pot-addled argument on Brad's deck, among the cigarette butts and beer bottles. Twenty-five years on, the debate still raged.

FUCK 1080!
STOP THE POISON

They found Leah's car at the end of this track. I imagined the splash as her wheels sank into muddy potholes, her wipers at full speed. What was she thinking as she bumped towards the trail head? Did she have her heating turned up high, for a few last minutes of comfort? Was she listening to the radio? *Perfect weather for finding Marchant's snails.* In a way, she died for those ancient, flesh-eating creatures.

•

I'd just pulled up at home when my phone vibrated in my pocket. Carmen, of course, sounding brisk. We're not good at apologies in my family; we're excellent at under-carpet-sweeping, though.

'We somehow got cut off,' she said.

'We did.' It was a useful fiction; we both bought into it. 'Dodgy signal.'

I let her talk while I carried in the shopping. This was no time to fall out with my only sister. Besides, she was making valid points. Even if we somehow arranged for carers to drive all the way out to Arapito, Dad's days of living alone there must be numbered.

'What about the dogs?' I asked. 'He loves them. They love him.'

'I know. But I can't offer Dad a home with my family, Emily. I just can't. I know you're judging me.'

'I'm not.'

'It's too much to ask of Richard and the kids. We're both working full-time, we're in a city, there's nowhere for the dogs. Dad would absolutely hate living with us. He's just . . . not that kind of man, is he? I sometimes wondered why he had children at all, or a wife.'

Once the shopping was unpacked, I poured a glass of chilled water, added a slice of lemon from the tree outside, and took it along to Dad. I found him asleep in the study, but as I lowered the glass to the desk he opened his eyes. He seemed disorientated, startled, even frightened.

'Hey, Dad,' I whispered. 'Just bringing you some water.'

He woke up properly then, and smiled at me. 'Oh! Thank you. You are so kind.'

There was no alternative to St Patrick's, I told myself as I threw our washing into the machine. No alternative at all. None.

SEVEN

The following afternoon found me crunching up the track towards Ira's cabin. Past the dam, a maze of cracks splitting its rust-coloured mud; past the woolshed and the yards. Cattle lay in patches of shade, chewing the cud and flicking their tails at the flies.

I'd left soup in the crockpot. Dad kept wondering what it was, lifting the lid and peering in. I only just stopped him from adding a cupful of salt. He seemed to have no tastebuds.

He was fretting about where I was going, and when I'd be back. He must have asked me ten times in the space of an hour. So I left a note on the kitchen table:

> *DAD*
> *I've gone to see Ira. I will be back by 6.30 pm.*
> *Everything is fine.*
> *Love,*
> *Emily X*

I was puffing up the steepest bit of track when Eddie rang.

'How're you feeling?' he asked me. 'Still jetlagged? Nice to be home after all this time?'

'Hilary Izzard is still haunting the place.'

He chortled, said he'd forgotten about that story, and I had a memory like an elephant. Then he began to talk about Felix. He didn't call Dad 'Dad' anymore. Apparently, when you develop dementia, your fatherhood is erased.

'Unsafe,' he said. 'Physically and financially. We're all worried he could be at risk of exploitation.'

'I know exactly who you mean,' I said. 'And it's ridiculous.'

'I hope you're right.'

I leaned against a fence post, silently seething while he waffled on and on like a gently crushing steamroller. He was using his counsellor voice, patient and empathetic. I imagined how fun it would be to blow a high-pitched referee's whistle down the line.

'It's becoming urgent,' he said. 'He needs to grant Carmen and me powers of attorney while he's still legally competent. I want to work *with* him. That's where you come in—to explain all of this to him. You're our woman on the ground.'

I could see the logic, but I couldn't bring myself to agree.

'He's still pretty sharp,' I said.

'But for how much longer? Did Raewyn tell you about the fire she had to put out in his kitchen? The thing is, Emily, you'll have left the country in a couple of weeks. I doubt you'll ever see him again.'

'Harsh.'

'Don't make life tougher for those of us who're doing the heavy lifting.'

'Tosser,' I muttered, once he'd rung off.

My schoolmate was lying on the grass outside his cabin, wearing shorts and a singlet, messing about with his quad bike. He had engine oil streaked down his arms and face.

'Who's a tosser?'

'My brother.'

He grinned as he pulled a wheel off the bike. He didn't comment. Didn't need to. We grew up together; we both knew Eddie.

Ira's cabin was built in the 1950s, designed for a single worker: one bedroom, a covered deck at the front, kitchen at the back. We always got together here on my rare trips home. I knew how it would be: a bit of chat, laughter, long silences. I plonked myself into the ancient sofa, while Ira disappeared into his even older and more ragged armchair.

The deck was shaded, the beer gloriously cold. I felt happier than I had in days. We lounged with our bare feet up on the handrail, swigging from bottles, staring at the view. You couldn't *not* look at Ira's view, because it was world-beating. We were at the back of the farm, where productive land merged into scrub and bush. The ranges were close: every valley, every face, every slip seemed unnaturally vivid, as though lit up for a photographic shoot. Just metres away, the ground plunged into a boulder-strewn ravine, forged over centuries by the Arapito stream. The water was low now, but when in flood it had the power to carry whole trees. If you followed it upstream from here, you'd come out halfway up Biddulph Road.

Ira asked how I thought Dad was doing. I told him the truth— that my father's mind was fading. He didn't always know who I was, he asked the same questions time after time. I got up and demonstrated how he sometimes walked with a new kind of care, as though afraid of forgetting where to put his feet.

My friend nodded gloomily. 'I've seen him do that. Poor old Doc.'

He recognised some of these signs, of course. When we were still at primary school, Manu was deteriorating. One day Ira whispered to me that his dad was going to die. 'But not for ages,' he added quickly. 'Not until I'm twenty, or even thirty.'

'And how's that boy of yours?' he asked now. 'Running the world yet?'

'He's in Jakarta,' I said, getting out my phone to show him some photos Nathan had just sent. Ira chuckled at my hostility to Ella, said he reckoned I'd be the tiger mum from hell and he felt sorry for the poor girl.

'You don't want to share him,' he said. 'It's always been just him and you.'

There was something in that. Nathan's father ran like a hare when I discovered a baby was on the way—quite right too, because he and I weren't remotely compatible.

'She mimics his voice,' I said.

'What's wrong with his voice?'

'That slight lisp. I've heard her teasing him about his freckles, his glasses, this little nervous twitch he gets when he's anxious. He really doesn't need to have his confidence torn down.'

'Nobody does,' said Ira. 'Another beer?'

He filled me in on the local gossip, the comings and goings of our schoolmates. Greta now owned the only hairdressing salon in Tawanui; Brad Taylor had made his fortune in the mines of Western Australia.

The beer was having more of an effect than it used to in my heyday. I was out of practice. Halfway through my third, I put my foot in it.

'You still go hunting up in the ranges, Ira?'

'Sometimes.'

'Still looking for Leah?'

He levered himself up without a word and stomped into the cabin.

Cursing my tactlessness, I laid the cold glass of the bottle against my cheek. 'Sorry,' I called through the open door.

He reappeared with two more opened bottles, one of which he handed to me before throwing himself back into his chair.

'I just want to know where she is,' he muttered. 'A shoe, water bottle—anything. I want the ranges to give a little bit of her back to us. I look at people walking around town, people I've known all my life. I've spent twenty-five years wondering if one of them killed her. Maybe by accident. I wonder if someone—or more than one person—knows where she is.'

'No local would do that.'

'Tawanui isn't full of saints. Imagine if she found herself sharing a hut with the wrong people. Alcohol and guns.'

He began to pick at the label on his bottle, peeling it from the glass. I could see the tension in his hands.

'That first day,' he said, 'your dad and I sprinted up to Biddulph's. Remember?'

'I remember.'

'I was running around like a headless chicken, yelling her name in case she could hear us. And I thought I heard her shouting back to me from somewhere down a really steep bluff. I was trying to climb down there when your dad stopped me. "Ira, that's not Leah's voice. It's your own." So I yelled again, and he was right, an echo came back. My own bloody voice. But sometimes I wonder . . . and I think what if she *was* down there, counting on me, calling for help?'

'They searched every inch around the bivvy,' I said. 'They'd have found her.'

We were both staring towards the saddle, as though we might magically spot an arrow marking Leah's location. The bivvy was *just there*, to the left of the slip.

During the search, a television news crew put a cameraman in a helicopter. That was when I began to understand that Leah might never be found. The footage roved over endless ravines and cliffs, spurs and valleys, shale slips, snow-covered uplands. Vast areas were submerged under rainforest canopy. Looking for a human being in such a pitiless wilderness was an act of faith— a needle in a haystack would be child's play by comparison. Modern trampers often carry GPS devices and personal locator beacons, and of course everyone has a mobile phone, though to this day you'd be lucky to get a signal in the Ruahines. Leah had none of these. She was on her own.

Ira downed half his bottle in one go, and said I wasn't to listen to a word of his bullshit, and anyway enough about him—how was my love life nowadays?

'Love life? Ha!' I scoffed, happy to change the subject.

'I thought there was some Spanish guy?'

'Portuguese. Estevo. Es-*te*-vo.' I imitated my latest ex's accent with a flamboyant wave of my hand. 'Nope. Long gone. He didn't get on with Nathan—how could anyone not adore my son? I'm all in favour of being single. Nobody wanting pieces of me, nobody demanding anything, nobody being a total knob.'

Ira snorted with laughter.

'How about you?' I asked.

'Nobody I'm going to tell you about.'

'Ooh!' I sat up straighter, intrigued. 'So there *is* someone?'

'Not really. Keep your hair on. It's not going anywhere.'

'Why not?'

'Not fair to her, is it? Every time I break something, or forget something, or drop something'—he held the green bottle close to his face, going cross-eyed as he focused on it—'I think: *Bloody hell, it this it? Huntington's?* I'm not asking anyone else to live like that.'

'Maybe she wouldn't mind.'

'She'd mind all right, if she'd ever seen what it looks like.'

Ira rarely mentioned the disease that killed his father—in fact, most people had no idea he was at risk. He didn't want to be defined by it. But I'd looked it up online. I knew he had a fifty-fifty chance of carrying the gene, and if he did, then he would eventually develop the disease.

'You haven't got it, though,' I said. 'Look at you! The picture of health.'

'That's true, but the fat lady hasn't quite sung yet. I'm forty-six. My dad wasn't diagnosed until he was . . . give you one guess.'

'Forty-six,' I said, as he mouthed the number along with me.

Fantails were flitting and piping in the trees above the ravine. Exquisite little birds. I watched them with absent-minded delight, but I was thinking about Ira's problem.

'There's a test, isn't there?'

'There is. Leah did it in Wellington. She was one of the very, very first. Typical of her. It came back negative—which was great, she could have kids and everything. Makes it extra fucked up that she never got to live her life. Anyway, Doc Kirkland once asked me if I wanted to be tested.'

'But you said no?'

'It's a pretty big decision. Most people say no. If it comes back negative—fantastic! I'm one hundred per cent in the clear. Then again, if it's positive . . .' He lowered his bottle to the floor. 'I just don't think I'm strong enough to find out whether there's a time bomb ticking inside me. Anyway, nobody knows what's around the corner. Whether I'm carrying the gene or not, all kinds of things might get me first: heart attack, cancer, quad bike accident. Whatever. Look at poor old Leah.'

Ira's life had been so tough, compared to mine.

He yawned and clasped his hands behind his head, flexing his shoulders. The inked pattern on his upper arm rippled.

'I don't need to know, and I don't want to know. Better just to Keep Calm and Carry On.' He said it in an over-the-top posh accent: *Keep Karm and Kerry Orn*. 'Like I am right now, on my porch with a few beers and a good friend.'

I leaned across and dragged his upper body into an awkward hug, despite his disgusted protests, and told him that I was honoured to be his good friend. I even managed to sneak in a kiss on his cheek before he pushed me away—'For God's sake, woman, three beers and you're anyone's.' But he was almost smiling.

EIGHT

I soon began to see the pattern. Dad had very good days, and very bad days, but as a rule he was best in the mornings, tired in the afternoons; and as the sun sank behind the peaks and the world darkened, his mind, too, filled with shadows. According to *Stranger in My Mirror*, this night-time confusion—'sundowning'—was a common phenomenon.

One evening, after I'd been home ten days or so, he began looking at his watch and mentioning how late it was. He thought I was some local who'd dropped by for a visit and was rapidly outstaying my welcome.

'It's been nice,' he said politely. 'But you should probably get off home now, shouldn't you? It's very late! Did you bring your car?'

We'd just had dinner together, and were doing the washing-up. I reminded him that I was staying, that I had a room down the corridor. He looked from me to the kitchen door and back again. He seemed mystified.

'You mean in this house?' he asked. '*I* live here, don't I?'

'Yes, you do. I've come from England to see you, Dad. I'm Emily.'

He was peering at my face, clearly trying to work out where he'd met this dumpy forty-something before.

'Emily,' I said again.

'Emily!' His puzzlement dissolved into a smile of heartbreaking affection, a smile I'd never seen before. 'Of course. Emily. How lovely that you're here. You've come a long way.'

He was flagging, his shoulders slumping, but he couldn't keep still. He roamed around the house, picking things up and putting them down again. A book. A wedding invitation. I switched on the television in the snug, but it only kept his attention for a few minutes. Even with all the windows and doors open, the evening felt oppressive and airless. I was wearing a cheesecloth sundress from Camden Market and the fabric was sticking to my back. I tried to console myself with the thought that I'd be back in London very soon, dancing to my own tune. Carmen and Eddie didn't want me interfering? Well, fine. Good luck to them! I'd be getting on that plane in less than two weeks' time. Definitely. *Definitely.*

Dad was on his feet again, more agitated than ever. He declared that he'd better make some dinner, and determinedly beetled off to the kitchen.

Sighing, I called after him. 'We've already eaten, Dad. Fish pie.'

He ignored me, and had begun to bang about in the cupboards when a message arrived on my phone. It was from my lodger, Ursula, who rented Nathan's bedroom.

Hi! How is NZ? I have a question. My sister Fran has to leave her flat NOW. She's finally split up with Otto! He changed the locks. Do you know of anyone nearby who has a room to rent? ☺ *Max is missing you. He says it's lonely all day without you!*

It was a blatant hint. I'd met Fran, knew about the volatile boyfriend. I was sure she'd take over my tiny boxroom studio in a flash if I offered it, but I needed that space for work, and for storing Nathan's things. The flat simply wasn't big enough for three adults.

Fanning myself with a newspaper, I began to type an answer.

Oh no, poor Fran! She can use my bedroom, just until I get back. But I'm sorry, I don't know of any

A crash from the kitchen had me on my feet. Dad was grabbing random things out of the fridge and freezer and pantry, dumping them all over the table. Leftover fish pie in its dish, apples and courgettes, trays of meat, half a pizza, soy sauce, a packet of peas, milk, pasta—more and more food joined the pile. His teeth were gritted as he moved from fridge to pantry to table and back again.

Nothing in life had prepared me for this. Nothing. Nor was there any magic formula in *Stranger in My Mirror*, though I'd now read it from cover to cover.

He is expressing emotions that he can't understand. Try to focus on the fear or anxiety behind his actions.

Well, that wasn't a whole lot of use right now, was it? Not with the entire contents of the freezer melting all over the table. We were nosediving down, down, down a rabbit hole and into Wonderland.

In desperation, I sent Raewyn a text:

Help!!! Please call Dad, he needs distracting!

Twenty seconds later, the house phone rang. Dad stopped throwing food around and hurried across the kitchen to answer it.

'Hello?' He listened for a moment, before a delighted smile transformed his face. 'Raewyn!'

From what I could overhear, her excuse for phoning was to ask what compost he thought was best for roses, and how did he tackle aphids? He drew up a chair from the table and sat down, crossing his legs.

'A tablespoon of washing-up liquid, and one of vinegar, in a litre of water,' he was saying. 'I spray it directly onto the leaves. Yes, very simple. Some people swear by a bit of canola oil, but I don't. Would you like me to bring you some of mine, ready mixed?'

Raewyn, you beauty. I crept around, dismantling his giant mound of food and wondering how on earth he would manage once I'd gone. The thought was heart-rending.

Life as a children's book illustrator was a precarious business. I did okay, better than most, but meeting my mortgage payments had been touch-and-go lately. If Fran moved into my room and paid rent, I might able to pay off my credit card; might even get that leaking shower fixed. *It wouldn't be forever, would it? Just until . . .*

What the bloody hell was I thinking? Sheer madness! Dad was already sick of me; half an hour ago, he'd been asking me to leave. I'd soon be home with my work, my friends, my flat, my routines. I had all kinds of events in my diary. I missed pubs and galleries and theatres, late-night shopping, buskers on the underground, the top decks of buses level with my kitchen window.

I finished typing my reply to Ursula:

I'm sorry, I don't know of anyone. I'll ask around. What about the flatting websites?

My finger hovered over the *send* icon.

NINE

I made my decision at three o'clock in the morning. It appalled me, but it was the only one I could make. Then I lay awake, thinking about the practicalities and dreading Mum's reaction. I finally fell asleep as the first birds began to stir.

•

Dad was having one of his good days. At coffee time he found the mugs with no trouble and remembered to turn off the gas ring. For now, at least, we were back out of the rabbit hole.

Morning coffee was already becoming our ten o'clock ritual. Sometimes we talked, sometimes we played chess, or did a crossword or Sudoku from the daily paper. Often we sat in companionable silence, watching cloud shadows scudding across the landscape. Precious hours. Despite the sadness and strangeness of my father's disintegration, I felt as though something was mending inside me.

I used to spend school bus journeys home thinking up questions to ask about medicine. I'd collar him earnestly over family dinner: *Dad, how does your brain get messages to your tongue so you can speak?* It never worked out as I'd hoped. He'd answer as though I was a third-year medical student, and it would be obvious that I wasn't understanding a word. Eddie would make a *duh* face, punch my upper arm and ask whether his message was getting to my brain. I'd yelp before the blow had even landed, and punch him back. Mum would sigh. Carmen would try to catch Dad's eye, clearly hoping he'd see her as the sensible one.

And Dad? He'd glance at his watch before sprinting away to chair a committee or see an urgent patient. I had no chance of engaging him. None of us had.

We were on our second mug of coffee when I finally came out with it. 'Um, Dad . . . I think I'd like to stay a bit longer. Would that be all right?'

'Stay where?'

'Here, with you. If that's okay.'

'Oh.' He looked mildly surprised. 'How much longer?'

'Maybe a few months.'

'Hmm.' He sipped his coffee.

'Would that be all right?'

'Of course! This is your home. Please stay as long as you like.'

I was taken aback. I hadn't expected him to agree so placidly, without even asking why I would want to stay.

'I imagine,' he said, 'that you think you ought to stick around to look after me. I imagine you've noticed that I'm losing my marbles. Right? No, no, please'—he held up his free hand—'don't play those games. I know. I may seem okay at this moment, but it's a very brief interlude. I come and go, don't I? I've got a large message pinned to the noticeboard in my study. It's in my hand-writing, so I assume I put it there to remind myself. Perhaps you spotted it?'

I shook my head. I hadn't noticed that particular sign.

'It says'—he underlined each word with his finger as he spoke—'*Felix—you—have—Alzheimer's.*' He turned his blue-eyed stare on me, smiling broadly as he uttered those awful words. Smiling.

I didn't know how to answer him.

'I've got the memory of a goldfish,' he said. 'Incidentally, it's not true about goldfish, did you know? That's a myth. Fish have excellent memories, which is why they shouldn't be kept in silly little bowls, swimming round and round a plastic castle and a hilarious No Fishing sign. So, alas, I don't have the memory of a goldfish. Wish I did. But one finds ways to manage. Little tricks. Notes to self. Leaving everything ready, easy to find. Routines. I got away with it for a long time. You last visited some years ago, didn't you, and never spotted it?'

'I should have, Dad. I really should have. I feel terrible.'

'No, no. I was very good at covering up. I retired as soon as I began to make mistakes, and there was nobody at home to notice. Raewyn did, of course, and helped me to deceive the world. I couldn't have managed without her. Anyway, they won't be treating me for this. I neither want nor deserve to prolong my life.'

'Dad . . .'

'It's all right. It's okay.'

We drifted into silence: an unhappy one on my part, though Dad seemed perfectly cheerful. A light aircraft was creeping along the bush line of the mountains, the drone of its engine just audible. Every few seconds the sun caught its fuselage, making the white dot gleam like a miniature star.

'I think that's Todd Tillerson,' said Dad. 'D'you know Todd? My lawyer. He's a local lad; did very well with a corporate law firm in Wellington, came back here, took over my affairs when . . . um, the last bloke, can't remember his name . . . when he retired.'

I squinted at the plane with new interest.

'I do know him. Todd went to Tawanui High—in the twins' year, I think. He had a car, used to drive himself to school. Very flash.'

Todd Tillerson and Leah were an item in the sixth form. Hot gossip. Eddie was beside himself with jealousy—*dunno what she sees in that dickhead, has to be the car*—but he needn't have bothered, because it only lasted five minutes. According to the grapevine, Leah dumped poor old Todd pretty unceremoniously.

'Well, now he flies a plane,' said Dad. 'Hang on . . . that reminds me. If you're staying a while, there's a document I want you to have. I'd better fetch it straight away, before I forget.'

He set off into the house at a rate of knots. I waited, mystified. He was back a minute later with a sheet of paper in his hand, looking triumphant.

'Hurrah! Found it! That's efficient filing for you.' He dropped back into his chair. 'This is my living will. It was drawn up by my lawyer, Todd Tillerson. I don't imagine you've met him.'

No more than ninety seconds had passed since we'd spoken about Todd. I tried to look thoughtful, my lips pursed as though I was racking my memory. 'Tillerson . . . Tillerson. Name rings a bell. Um . . . oh yes, he went to our school. He's a lawyer now, is he?'

'This'—Dad waved the paper over his head—'says they're not to muck about with resuscitating me, or treating me, or any other such nonsense. Now come on, for goodness' sake, don't look so shocked. You don't want me to go on forever, do you? I'd like you to keep a copy, because I may need an enforcer when the time comes.' He slid it across the chessboard table towards me. 'Not one hundred per cent watertight, I'm afraid, but it will certainly help, if it comes to the point.'

A pair of flies were buzzing in frantic circles around Raewyn's biscuit tin. I flicked them away but they came straight back, bringing three buzzing friends with them.

As I began to read, I forgot the flies.

MEMORANDUM OF WISHES AS A LIVING WILL

I, FELIX KIRKLAND, of Arapito homestead, Tawanui, now record the following:

I am aware that I have developed an irreversible, degenerative brain condition, as a result of Alzheimer's disease.

It is therefore my express wish that, should I for any reason become physically unable or mentally incompetent to express my opinion on the acceptance or refusal of life-saving treatment, the following must be considered to be my wishes:

1. *In the event of any cardiac arrest, I should receive no resuscitation of any kind, including cardiopulmonary resuscitation.*

2. *Should I develop any separate and life-threatening illness or infection, including pneumonia or heart disease, I should be given no active treatment or life-prolonging medical care whatsoever, save such as may be advised for the sole purpose of palliative care.*

3. *Should I become unable to swallow, then food and fluids should not be given me by any artificial means, except as is necessary to alleviate significant suffering.*

4. *Should I become unable to breathe unaided, then I should receive no artificial ventilation save as is necessary to alleviate significant suffering.*

He'd signed it, and his signature was witnessed by Todd and someone else.

'This is euthanasia,' I said.

'Not at all! I'm not asking anyone to bump me off—just don't go keeping me alive. Though, as a matter of fact, I'm in favour of assisted dying in certain circumstances. Some of my patients at the hospice would have liked to have the option, at least. There's a government committee looking at end-of-life choice. I've put in a submission.'

'But Dad, why give me this?'

'Because if I have a coronary event the paramedics aren't going to waste time digging through my filing cabinet, are they? They'll be too busy resuscitating me! Short of having this tattooed on my chest, it's hard to know how to stop them. I've given a copy to Marcia Ellis for my records at the health centre, one to Raewyn and now one to you. Your job is to wave this bit of paper under people's noses. Wave and shout! No resuscitation, no ventilation, no exceptions. Okay? Be my angel of death.'

I was reading the wretched thing for a third time.

'Listen.' He pressed his palms together, speaking with staccato precision. 'Imagine a . . . um, how can I best? . . . a mist, gathering in your brain. A heavy cloud. It shifts, it grows thicker, it obscures things—this, that. Imagine pieces of your mind being deleted. Words have gone. *Words!* Thoughts. All the things you keep in your head. Oh dear . . .' He squeezed his eyes tightly shut for a moment. 'You see, I'm having trouble even now . . . names elude you. Whole concepts mean nothing. You can't remember what you did just now. And yesterday? Yesterday doesn't exist at all. The world's like a drawing by . . . an artist, has a name like "mesh". Illusions. Puzzles.'

'Escher.'

'Escher. Like living in one of his drawings. You try to walk in what you think is the right direction but find you've moved the opposite way. You get lost in your own home. You're surrounded by complete strangers, but somehow they all know you—*Hi, Felix! Hi, Dad!* Who the hell are they?' He looked around, as though baffled by the crowd of imaginary strangers. 'They stare at you—*My God, he's gone mad*—as though you've grown another head. You put down your wallet, and when you look again, it's gone, disappeared, and you *know* it was right there. Somebody must have taken it! But who? You're completely alone. There's a cup of coffee on your desk, steaming hot—how the heck did it get there? Is there a hospitable ghost in this house, who keeps making you beverages?' He looked at me, blinking. 'Some days I still feel okay, but then the fog comes rolling in again, thicker than ever. It doesn't matter how much I kick and scream and try to grab on to things! Leah, I'm—'

'Emily.'

He blinked. 'Mm?'

'I'm Emily. Not Leah.'

'Emily. Not Leah. Of course you are. Emily, I'm lost in the mist, I'm sliding into an abyss. You can't begin to imagine the terror.'

He chuckled as he said those last words, his eyebrows raised high. He looked as though he was telling the punchline of a really funny joke, but his hands clung to one another for dear life.

'I know precisely how this will end. I've seen many people wandering through the same mist, all with the same lost look. Tomorrow I might have slipped so far into the bloody abyss that nobody will ever hear my voice again. They won't even hear me screaming. I could live for years like that. Years! Don't let me go on and on, all dribbling and terrified. Please, *please* . . . let me have a good death, if you can.'

I took a breath. I laid his document on the table.

'Okay, Dad. I've heard you.'

'You'll do it?'

'If I'm around when the time comes—*if* it comes, because you're ten times fitter than I am—I'll do my best to be your angel of death.'

He thanked me, took a gulp of coffee. I pictured myself getting between the hospital crash team and my dying father. I sincerely hoped I'd never have to do that.

'Have you shown this to Carmen?' I asked. 'Eddie?'

'Nope.'

'Maybe you should.'

'I think not. They would argue. And anyway, they aren't here.'

I folded the paper in half before slipping it into my pocket.

It was an awful pact we'd made, and yet I felt a childish satisfaction. Dad had confided in me. He'd never trusted me with anything more important than feeding the dogs. Now he'd made me champion for his good death.

TEN

When I phoned Mum to let her know I wasn't heading home as planned, she reacted more or less as I'd expected.

'I *knew* he'd twist your arm.'

'He didn't twist my arm at all.'

'Malcolm and I were coming to stay with you at Easter, remember?'

'I know. Sorry.'

'Well'—she paused, getting up the nerve to say something really bitchy—'you've always wanted Felix to value you. Now's your chance. I suppose he finally needs you.'

Ouch. That was way below the belt, and she knew it.

'I didn't mean that,' she said, after an icy silence at my end. 'Except we've all wanted him to value us, haven't we? I'm just afraid you're never going to come home. You're all so far away. All three of you, and my grandchildren.'

Nathan seemed far more enthusiastic about my news.

'Great!' he cried, when I called him. 'You're going to have some time with Grandpa.'

I arranged for the hire company to collect their car, which

they did at eye-watering expense. The most painful practicality was cancelling everything in my diary. Quite apart from Mum's visit at Easter, I had to cry off a fiftieth birthday bash, a long-planned week with friends in France, and the opening night of a local play for which I'd helped to paint the set.

But there was work to be done. My editor sent the text of the latest Buckingham Palace Cat story, typeset in the font and size in which it would eventually be published, along with a set of deadlines for each stage leading up to the date it went to print. It was past time for me to get cracking on *Admiral Flufflebum and the Christmas Kitten*. I gave my credit card a pounding by ordering art materials, a top-of-the-range printer and scanner, and setting up faster internet. Tools of the trade.

I chose Carmen's room for my studio. The light wasn't bad, with windows on two sides, and it was far bigger than my boxroom in the flat. I got Ira to help me carry in a table from the parlour. Apart from a load of junk in the wardrobe, all traces of my sister were long gone.

I also phoned Sarah Massey, the author who created Admiral Flufflebum and other colourful characters. Sarah and I had collaborated on eleven books now, and she'd become a close friend over the years. I was godmother to her youngest, four-year-old Toby. Her life was ordered beyond my wildest dreams: four children, a husband she still quite liked, a thriving career as the author of rhythm-and-rhyme picture books. She cooked like a goddess, drank too much red wine. All that good living had taken its toll on her waistline—even more so than mine—but unlike me, she didn't care. *I'm fat and happy*, she would say. *Better than thin and grouchy.*

She listened as I described how much Dad was struggling.

'That's terribly sad,' she said. 'For him and for you. Is this a long-term solution, though?'

'Probably not,' I sighed. 'But it'll do for now, at least. He's so diminished. I can't just walk away.'

'Well . . . you know where I am.'

She moved on to practicalities. Did I need her to do anything at the flat? Should she call in and check all was well there? Nathan wasn't due home any time soon, was he? If so, he was welcome to stay with her.

I thanked her, but Nathan wouldn't be back until next year.

A couple of days later, the Tawanui florist delivered a vast bunch of flowers. It really is the little things that make a difference. The message made me smile.

You're a better woman than I am.
Toby and I are right behind you!
Love,
S

•

I was setting up my new printer when the house phone rang. I rushed to snatch it up in the kitchen before it woke Dad, who'd dropped off in his deckchair in a shady corner of the garden.

'Kirkland's place,' I gasped, turning off the radio.

A male voice, politely hesitant. 'Ah, hello. Todd Tillerson here. Is Dr Kirkland available?'

I found myself smirking. The lawyer sounded so formal, so darned grown-up. It seemed only yesterday that he was wearing the school shorts and socks with their two white stripes, awkwardly holding hands with Leah. Most of us are just masquerading as adults, aren't we? All those forty- and fifty- and sixty-somethings, just a pack of school kids in disguise.

'Hello, Todd!' I cried. 'This is Emily.'

He seemed genuinely delighted, and we swapped life stories. He'd been back in Tawanui almost four years. Yes, he sometimes missed Wellington, but not the house prices or the commute. Yes, he did fly a Cessna, and it might well have been him we'd seen the other day. He became quite effusive when I told him I was planning to stick around for a while.

'That's wonderful for Dr Kirkland! He often talks about you.'

I snorted. 'I'm quite sure he doesn't.'

'He does. He's very proud of your career.'

What a fib! My father barely hid his disappointment when I chose to study fine art. Still, it was a white lie, kindly meant.

He said he was aware that Dr Kirkland had been having 'a few problems'. This was a typical Kiwi understatement. 'A few problems' was how people described their divorce, their bankruptcy, their metastasised cancer.

'Just a wild shot in the dark,' I ventured, 'but your calling today wouldn't be anything to do with my siblings, would it? Have they been hassling you about powers of attorney?'

'I'd better not comment on that—but I do need to see Dr Kirkland.'

'Those guys are far too interested in their inheritance. What makes them so sure they'll inherit anything? He might have decided to leave it all to his dogs. I hope he has. Actually, *has* he?'

Todd, I supposed, knew exactly what was in Dad's will. He probably drew it up. Still, he didn't take the bait. We agreed that I'd pick a morning when Dad was in good form, make an appointment—*just have a word with Sally*—and drop into his office.

As I put the phone down, I heard Dad out in the garden. He'd woken up and was chuckling at Gyp. *You're a clown! Yes, I know, you want to go and chase rabbits.* I stood at the kitchen window, listening as he prattled on. Our family always had dogs, but I'd never heard him talk to them so fondly, as though they were grandchildren. No, he'd never chatted to his real grandchildren like this either. Dementia had mellowed him.

The day was mellowing too, colour and contour draining from the landscape. I thought about Todd Tillerson's little plane, nosing along the bush line. Perhaps he, like Ira, had never stopped looking for Leah.

ELEVEN

June 1994

The news is out: Leah's missing. A procession of well-wishers arrive at Raewyn's house, caravans of friends and relatives bearing casseroles and tearful hugs. And words, and more words. So many words. *Leah will be fine, she knows her bushcraft! She'll be sitting out the weather. She'll walk out of there. She's her father's daughter. She's a survivor.*

The local search and rescue volunteers are coordinated by a bearded farmer called Dave Perry. According to Leah's notes, her route will have taken her across the uplands and along a knife-edge ridge before turning west into a steep, almost impenetrable area. There are few trails in there, but some of the old hands remember a derelict hut. Dad and two others hike in to have a look. They find nothing. The hut has collapsed, leaving a pile of rotting timber and tin. If Leah had sought shelter here, perhaps because of an injury, she'd have been disappointed.

Soon volunteers from all over the North Island are battling atrocious conditions as they join in the search. They pore over maps: *If she fell from the ridge* here or here, *where might she have ended up?* They lower themselves into gullies. They look at swollen rivers and try to calculate how far a body might be carried. Pilots from the aeroclub skim as low as they dare across the open tops. Leah is headline news in the national papers: SEARCH FOR LOST TRAMPER HAMPERED BY POOR WEATHER.

I was the last person to see her, and I long to be the one to save her. I borrow Dad's spare binoculars and spend hours scanning the mountains for a winking flash of reflected sunlight. I imagine Leah lying broken, using the silver paper from her chocolate to try to signal for help. I become fixated on that bar of Cadbury's. I picture her eking it out, allowing herself a square every day until the last one is gone.

Leah's a passionate conservation biologist; she's also young and photogenic, always a drawcard when it comes to scoring column inches and breathless daily updates: INTO THIN AIR: WHERE IS LEAH PARATA? Tall tales take wings and fly like fire-breathing dragons over the community of Tawanui. There's gossip about a violent boyfriend with gang connections, about dangerous people growing cannabis up in the ranges. In response to a police appeal, several callers report a dark-haired woman walking along State Highway 50 on the Friday evening. Someone saw her getting into a car. This sounds hopeful—until the woman herself comes forward. Her car broke down, she accepted a lift from a friend. She's alive and well, and she definitely isn't Leah Parata.

Meanwhile, some of Leah's university colleagues tell the police about nasty bruising on her face, arm and leg. It was some months ago, and she gave a plausible explanation—a collision with another pedestrian—but looking back, they wonder if she could have been a victim of violence? She's seemed distracted lately, or anxious, or maybe just overworked. Nothing you could put your finger on. In retrospect, they wonder whether she might have been in some kind of trouble.

Leah's housemates get in on the act. Their theory is that Leah has been secretly 'seeing someone', though they've never glimpsed this mythical person. She's been making phone calls from behind closed doors, abruptly ending them if anyone comes in. They found the toilet seat up, two wineglasses in the sink, but Leah denied point-blank that she'd even had a visitor. Why would she lie?

'It's all just gossip,' says Raewyn. 'What does any of that nonsense have to do with the Ruahines?'

Then, a breakthrough. Or not. Three men make contact with the police. They were actually on Biddulph Road very early on the Saturday morning, the night after Leah left. They'd planned a day's hunting and driven up there, but hadn't bargained on such grim weather. They stopped about halfway up the track and sat in their vehicle, smoking and yarning, debating whether to abandon their trip—which they later did.

While they were parked there, a tramper in a dark jacket (maybe blue or black?) passed them, walking from the direction of the trail head. The person's hood was up over their face, and their head was down, presumably against the rain. The three guys assumed at the time it was a man, but they couldn't now swear to it. They reckoned he or she might have been in a hurry, 'as though someone was after them'. One of the trio insists he glimpsed a blue, or green, beanie underneath the hood.

At this, the police take notice. Blue-green hat, dark jacket! Perhaps it was Leah? If so, good news! She was safely down from the ranges by Saturday morning. They appeal for the dark-jacketed hiker to come forward: *We just want to eliminate you from our inquiries. Anything you tell us will be dealt with in confidence. Please, whoever you are, make yourself known.*

Nobody ever does. The mysterious hiker is just one of many red herrings that flop about during the search. Maybe he or she was an overseas tourist, now long gone. I hear on the grapevine that the three hunters aren't very reliable witnesses; the police suspect it wasn't ordinary tobacco they were puffing that morning.

The strangest theory of all comes from Vince Price, after Leah has been missing for about four days. He's an electrician, called in by my boss to do some rewiring at the petrol station. His van has a ladder on the roof and VINCE PRICE ELECTRICAL painted in giant letters down both sides.

'No news of Manu Parata's daughter,' he remarks, as he puts away his tools.

'Not yet.'

'They'll never find her.' He scratches his nose, smiling at me. He's tall and twitchy. 'They can't.'

'Can't?'

'Nah. Because she's not up there anymore. She's been taken.'

The cheeriness of his tone is spine-chilling. I try to look politely interested while inching closer to the safe room, a cubby hole where employees can lock themselves away in the event of an armed robbery. Vince is obviously about to confess that he's murdered Leah. I'll be next on the list.

'Hold on to your hat,' he says, still beaming. 'You won't believe this. The best way I can describe them is to call them "beings". Not human. They come from an exoplanet in our own solar system.'

I listen, wide-eyed and slack-jawed, while he explains about these beings. He's seen their ship and heard their messages through the radio in his van. They'll never bring Leah back, but nor will they hurt her. He's rubbing his hands together, as though washing them under an invisible tap.

'She'll be happy,' he assures me. 'They like humans.'

At this, I'm overcome with nervous giggles.

He's offended. 'You think I'm talking rubbish.'

'I don't, Vince.'

'People disappear every week! Haven't you noticed? The police have a list going back for years. Hundreds and hundreds of missing persons. Where d'you think they've all gone?'

In his mind, this question is obviously the clincher. When I can't come up with a reply, he winks. Game, set and match.

The electrician hasn't been gone long when a police car turns in at the petrol station. Two affable men get out, both uniformed, wanting to talk to me about Leah.

'She have a current boyfriend, so far as you know?' they ask.

I shrug. 'If she did, he's probably in Wellington.'

'Nobody from around here?'

'They're all ancient history,' I tell them. 'She dated a guy called Todd Tillerson when they were at school, and my brother has been crazy about her forever, but Leah's *way* out of his league.'

They grin at this piece of sisterly bitchiness. Then they ask if I noticed any injuries on Leah last Friday, anything at all unusual. Did she seem frightened? Did she mention being in any kind of trouble?

I think back to those minutes with Leah. Her smile. Her confidence as she strode out to her car, pulling on that vivid beanie.

'She seemed fine,' I said. 'She was only after a bar of chocolate. She told me stuff about her snails. Um . . . we talked about the rain. I'm going to South America soon, to do some volunteer work, then to the UK. She asked about that.'

Could I confirm what clothes she was wearing? That was easy. Hiking kit. A black jacket, could well have been navy—her mum would know. Waterproof trousers. Boots with red laces. A beanie, very bright turquoise.

Any unusual vehicles in the area? Nope. I served every customer who came through that day, and there was nothing out of the ordinary about any of them. I knew just about everyone, by sight at least.

Anything I wanted to add?

Just that it was raining cats and dogs, I reminded them. Heavy cloud, right down to the foothills. She was setting out into terrible weather, and she knew it, but she said it made it easier to find snails.

They nodded sadly. They knew about the weather. Anything else?

I tried so hard to remember anything that might help, anything at all.

I even told them about Vince Price. Yes, they sighed, they were aware of Mr Price's theory. He'd called the hotline a number of times. But they felt, on balance, taking everything into consideration, that alien abduction was unlikely.

•

The first notes of despondency began to creep into newspaper headlines: IRA PARATA: 'I STILL HAVE HOPE. IF ANYONE CAN SURVIVE UP THERE, IT'S MY SISTER.' And on the television news: *Hopes fade for the missing conservationist.*

I hear Dave Perry explaining to Raewyn that Leah may have become disorientated in rain and low cloud. The most experienced trampers and hunters can and do get lost, he tells her. She could have slipped and fallen down a bluff or gully, or into a flooded river. In sub-freezing conditions, with high winds, she'd be fighting a losing battle with hypothermia.

'Will she be suffering at this moment?' asks Raewyn. 'If she's up there hurt, and still alive, is she suffering?'

Dave, like my father, has been a volunteer searcher for years. He's rescued people in the last stages of hypothermia; he's recovered the bodies of those who couldn't be saved. He looks at Raewyn for a long moment before shaking his head.

'I don't think so,' he says. 'She'd probably just fall asleep.'

Poor Raewyn looks out at the snow-clad peaks, and shudders.

•

One sunrise brings the sight of a heavy fall of snow on the ranges. I huddle in my warm bed, looking out at the murderous beauty and shivering with horror for Leah. Later, Dave Perry rings to say that the official search is being called off.

This is the only time I've ever seen my father cry. He looks spent, his unshaven cheeks hollow. He's fifty years old, give or take. Until this week he could easily have passed for thirty-five, but not anymore. The tragedy has depleted him. He looks crushed, as though physically carrying some great weight. He's pulled a calf muscle, which is the first injury I can remember him sustaining. He keeps leaning down to massage it. I'm unnerved—okay, I'm also jealous—to see my granite father so close to collapse. But he's known Leah since she was eleven; he walked beside her family during Manu's lingering death. Of course he's devastated. We all are.

'The snow,' he groans, staring towards the peaks. 'She'll be covered in snow.'

Mum makes him a cup of coffee and tells him to get some rest. She's due to fly back to England tomorrow.

'Not yet,' he says. 'I must go and see Raewyn.'

'Raewyn's got plenty of support! There are about fifty people in her kitchen.'

'She's my patient.'

Mum shrugs, grabbing her jacket from its hook. 'Okay, okay, okay.' She sounds weary. 'Do whatever you want.'

She bangs out through the sliding door. Seconds later I see the glow of her cigarette on the porch. It's like old times, and not in a good way.

•

The next morning I drive Mum down to Palmerston North airport, leaving extra time because of the weather.

'Wouldn't it be lovely if you were coming with me?' she sighs, and I agree. I wish she wasn't leaving so soon.

'The last time I made this journey,' she adds wistfully, as we pass the *Fortieth Parallel* marker, 'I was leaving my husband forever. Leaving my children. I was most worried about Eddie; he wasn't in a good place. He worked *so* hard to try to get into medicine. To be like Dad, to make Dad proud. That was his dream.' She shrugs. 'A pipe dream.'

'And I was eighteen.'

'Yes, you were only eighteen, and I'm sorry. I did invite you to come with me.'

Which is true, though she knew darned well I'd refuse. I was a first-year university student—a small-town girl hitting the big city and partying like there was no tomorrow. No *way* was I giving up all that lovely freedom.

I mutter something passive-aggressive about how it was fine, she had her own life to lead, *yada yada yada*. I hope she'll have the tact to drop the subject, because I haven't really forgiven her at all.

Tact was never her strong point. Two minutes later, she's chuckling. 'I laughed out loud when I stepped on that plane. The cabin crew must have thought I was a real old soak. I told them, *I'm not drunk—I'm laughing because I won't have to look at those bloody mountains anymore!*'

I'm concentrating on the road, which is slick and treacherous, especially when mud-splattering cattle trucks thunder past in the other direction. My windscreen wipers aren't up to the job.

'Sorry, I'm being crass.' Mum's suddenly sober again. 'I make it sound as though I didn't care. Of course I cared. You were too young; what kind of a mother was I? And I still love Felix, whatever the hell that means . . . but he's so relentlessly bloody perfect, isn't he? And relentlessly miserable—that's what brought me down in the end. I tried to fit in. I got that job at the library.'

'You did.'

'I mean . . . there wasn't even a hairdresser in Tawanui when we first arrived, d'you remember? No traffic lights! I didn't know a single thing about pickling gherkins, or bottling peaches, or having baking days. Felix lives for all this'—she gestures out of the window—'this nothingness, this wilderness. But it terrifies me. We've sod all in common. He had no interest in me, emotionally or intellectually or . . .' She turns up the heating, rubbing a hole in the condensation on her window. 'I wasn't asking for a grand passion, but not even to be mates with your husband?'

I don't want to hear about my parents' love life. I turn on the radio, but that doesn't stop her.

'I was depressed here,' she says. 'I ended up on little yellow pills. Did you know?'

'I didn't. That's awful.'

'Felix couldn't help me. He couldn't even help himself.'

Our route to Palmerston runs through the Manawatu Gorge. A wall of rock and scrub edges the narrow road to one side; on the other is a blood-freezing drop down to the river. Its headwaters are in the Ruahine Range. I slow to a crawl, steering around piles of boulders and mud brought down by the storm.

'Awful to think of Leah,' says Mum. 'Still up there. What if they never find her? What if they never know what happened, or where she is?'

The Manawatu surges through the gash in the landscape, swollen by rain and snowmelt. Murderous, muddied currents.

Mum covers her eyes with her hand.

'Imagine never knowing,' she says.

TWELVE

March 2019

The new normal. I surprised myself. I took one day at a time, got on with my work and let the weeks drift past.

I finished and delivered an existing project, a first reader, and was paid for it. Meanwhile I'd begun work on a storyboard for *Admiral Flufflebum and the Christmas Kitten*: a rough layout, thumbnail sketches of various sizes with random ideas scribbled among them. The largest were double-page scenes, but miniature images were dotted through the text: a kitten's tail and ears appearing from behind a giant exclamation mark, the Admiral leaping from one word to another. My sketchbook was already full.

'How are you feeling?' asked Sarah, when I phoned her on her birthday.

'Very guilty! I promised to take Toby to Legoland next holidays. I bet he hasn't forgotten.'

'Legoland will still be here when you get back. I've got a wonderful man lined up for you. Soon as you're home, I'm going to get you both over for dinner. He's melancholy and creative, just your type.'

'I don't think I have a type.'

'He's only been divorced once. Not a bad record.'

A thin parcel arrived in the post that morning. It was from Mum: a glossy Yorkshire Dales 2019 calendar, with glorious photographs. *I thought it might help Felix's memory to look at scenes from home*, she wrote.

'How very kind,' said Dad, and he put it up on the kitchen wall. The image for March was of Fountains Abbey, with blooming daffodils in the foreground.

I set up shop in the kitchen, ironing a pile of Dad's clothes. He'd done all these things for himself in the past, but nowadays he struggled. I'd forbidden Raewyn to act as his housekeeper any longer.

Seeing me with the ironing board out, Dad decided that today was the day to polish his shoes. This was one of his favourite chores. Perhaps it made him feel he still had some kind of control. He'd lined up a row of brogues and hiking boots on newspaper on the kitchen table and was wielding his age-old shoe-cleaning kit: dubbin and polish, brushes marked *ON* and *OFF*. We had Mozart's Clarinet Concerto on the stereo, the doors and windows open to catch any breeze. We were content.

'My mother spent half her life ironing,' he remarked, as I sprayed mist onto one of his shirts. 'Starched everything. Sheets, pillowcases, underwear! Shirt collars so stiff they hurt when they rubbed against my neck. She'd have starched Helen and me too, if she could. I remember that very strong smell of laundry.'

He had such vivid recollections of his childhood. They seemed to be bursting into life now that his short-term memory was failing.

'What was Nan Kirkland really like?' I asked. 'Mum's not a fan, I know.'

He was prising off the lid of a tin of brown polish. 'Thing is, my mother had *faith*.'

'I know that.'

'Yes . . . we're not talking about a bit of church on Sundays. Hers was the real thing: unequivocal, unquestioning faith. Imagine that! Her belief in a rigid moral system, imposed by a higher power, was at the core of everything she did, or thought, or said.' He dipped his brush into the tin before dabbing soft polish over a boot. 'This was the 1940s and '50s, remember. She got mixed up in a very conservative church. Even by the standards of the day, that mob were zealots.'

'Sounds grim.'

He raised his eyebrows as he picked up the other boot.

'Mother once caught my sister and me sitting in the same bed. It was pocket money day, and I'd bought sweets. We'd made a tent with the blankets and my torch, and were having such a lovely time! A midnight feast.'

'Cute.'

'Mother didn't think so. She shook with rage. Shook! *What's going on? What's going on?* I can see her now!'

Nut-brown polish splattered around the table as he imitated his mother's fury, wild-eyed, brandishing both fists.

'She hauled me right off Helen's bed, threw me on the ground. My arm hurt for days. In retrospect, I'd diagnose a moderate soft tissue injury. *If I ever, ever catch you in her bedroom again! If I ever catch you touching one another again!*'

I'd put down the iron. 'Touching?'

He shrugged, calmly resumed polishing. 'Helen was snuggled up to me. We were great friends. After that, I was always locked in my room at night. Father fixed a bolt on the outside of my door.'

'He did *what*?' My jaw dropped in outrage. 'He was as bad as her!'

'In his way. I've fewer memories of him. He was conscripted, fighting in Burma when I was born. Nobody knows what happened to him there, and he never said a single word about it, but Mother said he came home a different man. Black moods, nightmares. He wasn't interested in us. I don't imagine she was an amiable wife.'

'PTSD?'

'They didn't call it that back then.'

'Your parents were totally screwed up.'

He seemed to examine the idea, his head on one side. 'Yes, I agree entirely with that assessment. Mother honestly believed that a six-year-old and an eight-year-old might be harbouring incestuous passions. We grew up with their faith, of course, but I had an ep—an epi . . . oh, damn!'

He banged his forehead with one fist, while I feverishly hunted for his lost word. *Epileptic fit? Epidural?*

'Words, words,' he grumbled. 'Tip of my tongue . . . you know, when the scales fall from your eyes.'

'Epiphany?'

'Epiphany.' He exhaled in a rush. 'Thank you. I had an epiphany, when I was fifteen or so. Jesus *wasn't* watching me! He *couldn't* hear my private thoughts! Gosh, that was life-changing. I tried to help Helen to see what I could see, but I failed. If only I could have got through to her, I believe she'd be alive today.'

I was all ears now. Aunt Helen was a mythical creature, her short life over long before I was born. The subject was taboo in our family. We knew only that Dad once had a younger sister, and she died, and that was sad.

'What happened to Helen?' I asked.

He picked up another shoe, holding it in both hands.

'She fell pregnant at the age of seventeen. The boy was from the same church, neither of them knew anything about contraception. I suspect Helen knew nothing about sex either, since it was never mentioned. She had no idea she was pregnant. She went to the doctor with vomiting and . . . oh dear, my poor little sister. Imagine! An unmarried teenage mother, in that church, in the 1960s. The sky had fallen in! Deep, deep disgrace. The two families got together, the young couple were rushed into marriage. Just kids, the pair of them. And'—he shook his head as he unlaced the shoe—'there were complications in the pregnancy. Of course, abortion was absolutely out of the question, a mortal sin, even though Helen was risking her life to carry that child to full term. By getting pregnant, she'd become a vessel. Expendable.' Dad put the shoe down. 'I was a medical student at the time. The first I knew was a telegram notifying me that Helen had died, and so had her baby son.'

The iron stood upright, hissing steam. The shoes lay half-polished. Mozart played on, unheeded.

'How could you ever forgive your parents?' I whispered.

'Why d'you think I was so determined to emigrate? Why do you think I never went back, not even for their funerals—not even to save my marriage?'

I'd never questioned his keen desire to move all this way. I'd simply assumed he was drawn by the lifestyle, the space, the weather.

A speck of polish had smeared his sleeve. He took a hand-kerchief from his trouser pocket, licked it and dabbed at the spot.

'Mother had a real hang-up about touching people. Any touching at all. I never saw her and Father embrace, let alone kiss. I have no idea how we were conceived. I remember one awful time, when she was about three, Helen fell over and was crying. When I ran to comfort her, Mother slapped my leg. I crept off and got a biscuit from the tin and sneaked it to her.'

My heart ached for those two little children. If Nan Kirkland were still alive, I'd have phoned her up to tell her she was evil.

'What the hell was *wrong* with her?'

He was still dabbing at the speck of polish. 'I have a theory about that, actually. D'you want to hear it? Gosh, the family skeletons really are trooping out of the cupboard! Well, Mother was estranged from her elder brother. Harry.'

'Harry.' The name rang a bell. 'Is he the one who died in the war?'

'That's right. Killed in North Africa. My grandfather—his father—used to raise a glass to Harry over Christmas lunch every year. *To Harry*. But my mother would leave the room. She never, ever spoke his name. She had no photos of him, nothing. When I asked about him she went quite white. She said she hadn't seen him since she was thirteen, and he was a pervert who would have ended up in jail if he hadn't got himself killed. She thought that bullet was God's judgement on him.'

'Hang on. You mean Nan's brother'—I paused, blinking, as the implications sank in—'he maybe did something to . . . you think that's why she yanked you out of Helen's bed?'

'I mean precisely that. I suspect her parents disbelieved her, or at least tried to hush it up. People didn't talk about such things in those days.'

It was disturbing, and yet it made sense. This unmentionable, long-dead Uncle Harry might be ground zero to all the dysfunction in our family. Dad knew his memory banks were being wiped clean. He was passing his stories on to me. I was the keeper of secrets now.

'Maybe your mum was a victim,' I said. 'But it's no excuse for being such a bitch to you and Helen.'

'People in glass houses.' Dad had picked up the *OFF* brush and was scuffing it across the toes of a boot. 'I'm afraid I wasn't a much better parent.'

For years, I'd complained bitterly about exactly this: that he'd barely been present in my childhood, uninterested, incapable of showing affection. Now I found myself hotly defending him.

'You never locked me in a room!'

'Pretty low bar, isn't it?'

Putting his boots to one side, he began to pack up the shoe-shine kit. It took him a while to stow everything away. He seemed suddenly deflated. His energy was gone, his shoulders drooping.

'One day,' he said quietly, 'you'll be ashamed of me. You'll know what I really am.'

'Rubbish.' I turned away from him to fill my iron with water from the kettle. 'That's Nan talking, isn't it? Nan's guilt schtick.'

It wasn't until I turned back that I realised I was talking to an empty room. I heard Dad's steps in the corridor, his study door shutting. Mozart played on.

THIRTEEN

Todd Tillerson's office was a converted villa on a side street in Tawanui, with a magnificent wisteria curling over the porch. An aquamarine sign at the door proclaimed that this was *Smith and Harley, Legal Services*.

The office administrator was one of those well-dressed, grey-haired women who still go jogging in their sixties and make me feel like a squashed elephant. Bet she came first in the school cross-country.

'Dr Kirkland,' she cried, as soon as we set foot on the plush carpet. 'How lovely to see you!'

'Likewise.' Dad shook her hand. 'How are you? How is your family?'

She talked animatedly for several minutes about somebody called John who was getting married, and wasn't that funny, because Dr Kirkland had helped to deliver John all those years ago, breech delivery!

'Very funny,' said Dad. 'Ha! Well! What good news. I'm so pleased for you. My very best wishes to him, and to all.'

She asked if we wanted tea or coffee. Todd would be with us in a few minutes, apparently.

Once she'd bustled off, Dad leaned his head close to mine. 'I have *no* idea who that woman is,' he whispered, with an anxious glance at the empty reception desk.

I laughed. He didn't. He looked fearful.

'She seems to think she knows me,' he said.

'She *does* know you, Dad.'

'But I've never clapped eyes on her in my life.'

When I made this appointment two hours ago he'd been on the ball, enthusiastic about our coming in to meet Todd. Since then, he'd steadily deteriorated.

A tray with coffee arrived. Dad gripped his cup. His hands were shaking. 'Is this place a doctor's surgery?' he asked me, as he lowered his head to sip.

'Lawyer.'

'I'm pretty sure we've come to see a consultant of some kind. Are we in Hastings hospital?'

'No, no. It's okay, Dad. This is Todd Tillerson's office. The lawyer.'

'What's the date today? I have to know the date. I have to get it right.'

I told him the date. His lips moved as he repeated it.

'They always ask the date,' he said. 'It's to test whether you've lost your marbles. They ask the date, the day of the week. Then they ask, "Who is the monarch?"'

Coffee dripped onto his hand. I took the cup from him while he mopped with his hanky.

A minute later, he nudged me. 'What's the date?'

I told him again. Wednesday, 13 March 2019. He produced a biro from the inner pocket of his jacket and wrote laboriously on his own wrist, asking me to repeat the information halfway through.

Wed 13/3/2019

'D'you have a comb?' he asked. 'I must make myself presentable. They notice these things. I'm ashamed of my hair.'

I was fishing in my handbag when Todd burst through a door—shirtsleeves, no tie. He showed us into his room.

'Good to see Sally's looked after you,' he said, gesturing at our coffee.

'Very kind,' murmured Dad, while Todd made self-deprecating jokes about how Sally was the real power in his office, even the wisteria obeyed her.

Todd's office window looked across the school playing fields towards the ranges. His desk was about the size of a tennis court, which put a fatuous smirk on my face because Sarah had a theory about men with giant desks. It involved an inverse proportion. Most people would call the lawyer attractive, as men in their early fifties go. Dark hair flecked with grey, a neat beard—I'm not really into beards, but I had to admit that Todd pulled it off. Heavy-rimmed glasses. Brown eyes, with deep smile lines at their corners.

I was nervous on Dad's behalf, but Todd steered our meeting with endearing tact. He explained that, back in 2016, Dr Kirkland had decided to put his affairs in order.

'Your father was perfectly capable of giving coherent instructions on that date,' he said, looking at me. 'I asked his doctor, Marcia Ellis, to make a statement to that effect. I have it here—my trump card!' He opened a file. 'I made a note of everything we discussed.'

I watched him, intrigued. I had no idea where this was going.

'He feared his health was letting him down, didn't you, Dr Kirkland?' He smiled at Dad. 'Yes. So we discussed the appointment of a person with enduring powers of attorney, authorised to make decisions about management of his finance and property as well as his future care and welfare—a kind of insurance, in case the day should come when he isn't able to make those good decisions for himself.'

'That's what my sister and brother are talking about.'

'They are.' He met my gaze. 'Um, look, this is a bit delicate.'

'Spit it out, Todd.'

'Carmen and Eddie were the two people at the top of Dr Kirkland's list . . . by which I mean the list of those who must *not* get any power, under any circumstances.'

'Top of the blacklist!'

This was priceless news. I didn't even try to suppress a gurgle of laughter.

'*I deeply love and respect my elder children*'—Todd was reading from the memo in his file; he couldn't quite smother a grin—'*but I fear that their priorities may not, in the future, be aligned with mine.*'

'Wow.'

'Mm. The upshot is that, three years ago, Dr Kirkland gave me clear instructions regarding who he'd prefer to appoint, if possible. And it was you.'

I gaped at him, genuinely baffled.

'I don't even live here.'

'No. I advised against it for that reason, and he held off. But now you're back in the country indefinitely, and I gather there's been a new diagnosis, so . . .' He glanced at Dad. 'This might be a good time to get the ball rolling. I understand he still wishes to appoint you. Is that right, Dr Kirkland? Yes.'

I skimmed through the memo. There it was, in black and white. Dad had nominated me as a person he could trust. His second choice was Todd. According to the date, he made this decision just days after Nathan and I were last in Tawanui.

'Dad, why?' I asked, pressing his arm. 'I haven't been around. You've hardly seen me in twenty-five years. I've been a terrible daughter.'

He patted me absently, as though I were Gloria.

'The twins . . . very dear to me, of course, but I'm not sure they see things as I do. I'm not entirely convinced that they like me very much. I don't think I've had a real conversation with either of them for many years, and they're sometimes a bit, um, a bit ma—... damn! What is that word?'

'Mad?' I suggested.

'Not mad. Though Eddie, in the past ... No, this word means something like, um, like medals. Begins with M.' He tapped his knuckles on his temple. 'Oh, my stupid brain!'

I squinted, dredging for the right word. 'Money-grubbing? Materialistic? Mercenary? Ooh, what about mendacious?'

'No, no—medals.'

'Meddlesome?' suggested Todd.

'Meddlesome. That's it.' Dad sighed, a heaving breath that lifted his whole chest. 'They don't listen to me at all, they just say I can't manage. I feel as though they want me to fail. They're keen for me to move into a little room in St Patrick's. Can you imagine? I'm far younger than most of the residents there. I like my own home, my own things. You can't even see the ranges from St Patrick's. And what about my dogs? And what about Raewyn?'

He kept smoothing his hair with one hand—again and again, a tense, compulsive movement. The blank look was beginning to cloud his features. I needed to take him home.

'Have you told Carmen and Eddie?' I asked Todd.

'Not yet. Would you like me to write to them?'

'Rather you than me.'

He caught my eye for a split-second. I had to admit that his smile was charming.

•

'Home again,' I said, as we turned in through the road gate.

Dad wound down his window, letting heat and dust pour into the car. Sheep were clustered in the shade of the stand of macrocarpas by the derelict woolshed. I looked up at the tallest tree with its spreading boughs, and allowed myself a little smirk of . . . what? Triumph?

I was ten years old and about to die, my feet slipping off a flimsy branch at the very top of that tree—eight metres high, they told me—fighting to keep my balance while Eddie thrashed the bough up and down. He'd lost his temper because I won the tree-climbing race again, and I was crowing like a rooster about being the champion. I always won. I was no athlete, but I was the family maestro at climbing trees back then, when my muscle-to-weight ratio was the precise opposite to what it was now.

Carmen was too adult and dignified to climb trees. She was standing over at the fence, talking to the ponies. But she saw what happened. I knew she did. She *must* have.

I remembered every detail of the fury on my brother's face as he reached for my branch with his gibbon arms; still felt that ghastly, visceral terror as I tried desperately to hold on—*Please stop! I'm going to fall! Stop, Eddie!* He did stop, but not until I'd crashed through the springy foliage—from one bough to another, falling, falling—with a long screech of panic that had Mum sprinting from the house.

I was very lucky, she said later, because all those pliant evergreen branches bent as I fell, and slowed me down. She bundled me into the car and drove to Dad's surgery; he suspected I might have a head injury as well as a broken arm, and rushed me up to Hastings hospital. I don't remember anything about that journey, or the next few days. I ended up with a plaster on my arm but the bang to my head was the real problem. My brain felt foggy for years. I dropped from the top groups for reading and maths, groups Ira and I were in together, and ended up in the bottom ones.

Did Eddie get into trouble? Of course not. These things were never his fault.

'He didn't mean to do it,' Mum insisted, when I complained—slumping at the kitchen table with my arm in a sling. 'He feels awful about it. Life isn't easy for Eddie, you know.'

'I was trying to save you,' said Eddie.

'You were *not*.'

'I grabbed that branch to steady it, 'cos I could see you were wobbling.'

'You bloody liar!' I couldn't believe the brass neck of him. 'You tried to kill me!'

Mum was tight-lipped. 'That's a very serious allegation to make, Emily. And it's a silly one.'

I burst into tears. It was so wrong, so unfair. 'Carmen saw him! Tell her, Carmen.'

Mum's gaze swivelled to my sister, who had a spoonful of ice cream halfway to her mouth. Carmen froze with the spoon in midair. I saw her exchange glances with her twin. We all waited.

'I didn't see Eddie shaking any branch,' she said. 'Sorry, Emily. I think your concussion has got you confused.'

Then she calmly tucked into her ice cream—hokey-pokey, as I recall—while I ran to my room and sobbed.

That old tree was looking ragged now. Eddie had turned into a respectable addiction counsellor with receding hair, a slight paunch and his first grandchild. He ran professional development workshops all over the country, and in his spare time volunteered as a mentor for kids in care. Yes, my jerk of a brother was now the kind of guy who ends up with a Queen's Service Medal.

By the time we left the offices of Smith and Harley, I'd signed on all the dotted lines. I agreed to be appointed attorney because it was Dad's wish, and because I really did want to help him to stay in his own home for as long as possible.

It had nothing—*nothing*—to do with scoring the deciding goal in some invisible game against my siblings. Nothing.

●

The rest of that day was a good one, by the standards of our looking-glass life.

We got the ride-on mower out of the shed. Dad could still drive it, even if his route was pretty haphazard. Big success. While he was meandering around the lawn, I chatted to Nathan on Messenger. I showed him Dad mowing; he demonstrated how well his Indonesian was coming on. He said he was just a beginner, but to his proud mother he seemed completely fluent.

Dad and I spent the evening watching a history documentary on Netflix. Or, rather, he stared at the screen while I played about with sketches of palace horses. I needed to create personalities for them, to bring Sarah's story alive: one shy, another supercilious, another motherly.

When Eddie phoned to talk to Dad, I eavesdropped shamelessly on their conversation. I wondered whether he'd already heard from Todd, and braced myself for a massive showdown. None came.

'All well in your world?' Dad was asking.

I noticed how intently he listened to Eddie's answer, while mumbling little responses, just as he had when talking to Sally earlier. *Uh-huh. Mm. Really?* He was a magpie, poised to snatch at any valuable trinket of information. I suspected he'd been using this technique for years.

'Oh, that is good news,' he cried suddenly. 'She has an interview? Wonderful!'

He listened again.

'Well, that's great. Must be a weight off your mind . . . no . . . well, of course. As you say. Uh-huh. Mm.'

This performance went on for ten minutes. I was watching a magic trick performed by a desperate wizard. I was learning how to spot the smoke and mirrors. Dad kept up his end of the discussion without volunteering a single name, nor a single piece of independent information. He simply reflected back everything Eddie said, even his tone of voice, his emotion. The result was a slightly stilted, almost-normal-for-Dad conversation. It was impressive. I listened, silently applauding.

'I'm watching television,' he was saying. 'Yes. What are we watching? Oh, the usual kind of rubbish. I'm with, um . . .'

I glimpsed a wide-eyed spark of panic as he turned his head to look at me. I gave him a double thumbs-up, whispering, 'Tell him Emily, his sister, says hello,' and he nodded gratefully.

'With Emily. She says hello! Your sister! Yes, she's with me now. She's . . . well, she's drawing in a book. Lovely pictures of horses. Yes, yes, it's very nice that she's staying so long. You're right, good to have someone in the house. Would you like to speak to her? Another time. Well, I'd better let you go.'

As soon as the call was over, he collapsed into a chair. Pulling off the magic trick had sapped his energy. This was life for him, day after day. One long, relentless, exhausting act. He could never let down his guard.

'Is it late?' he asked, with his eyes closed. 'Feels pretty late. I think I'll turn in.'

We said goodnight. I listened as his bedroom door closed behind him.

He was good at playing a part. In fact, he was turning out to be quite the master of disguise. I hadn't known that about him.

FOURTEEN

It was a full week before Todd's news reached Carmen and Eddie, setting off more hysterical squawking than a fox in a henhouse.

The first voice message on my phone was my sister's, quavering with hurt and a light frosting of hysteria. *Oh hi, Emily, it's me. I mean . . . okay, um . . . I'm just a bit surprised, to be honest; this has come out of the blue. I'd have expected him to speak to us first, at least. Thing is, you haven't been here, have you? You haven't actually been here. Anyway, whatever. If that's what he wants . . . but I mean, is it what he wants? Is it really? Call me back.*

Eddie contented himself with a terse text: *Need to talk.*

'Oh, sod off,' I said aloud, deleting everything.

There was a far more pleasant message from Todd, who suggested I might call in sometime that day. He had documents for me to sign, he said, and one or two matters to discuss. No need to bring Dr Kirkland. I was ready to bet that one of those 'matters' was called Carmen and the other Eddie.

I'd got up early to work, and was on a roll despite the racket Gyp had been making all morning. I suspected a couple of newlywed rats had built their nest right underneath Carmen's built-in wardrobe, because the dog kept whining and scrabbling on the floor in there. In the end I shut him out of the room.

My current task was to expand on my thumbnail sketches, drawing them full-size and with more detail. The aim was to create a mock-up of the finished book, getting a feel for how everything worked in the space, including the valleys between double pages. Dear old Admiral Flufflebum would soon be winding himself around the royal legs, snoozing in the royal stables, stopping to lick his front paw and chasing George, an adorable abandoned kitten, across the thirty-odd draft pages of Sarah's story.

I drove into town after lunch and found Todd in a jovial mood, which seemed to be his default setting. A bouncy Tigger; I tend to go for angst-ridden Eeyores. He pulled on his jacket, offering to buy me coffee at Forty Degrees, one of Tawanui's two cafés. The place used to be dire: clouds of flies and the grumpiest service in the Southern Hemisphere.

'You won't recognise the joint,' the lawyer assured me as we strolled along the wide pavement, in the shade of metal awnings. 'They roast their own coffee. Award-winning pies.'

He was right. Forty Degrees had been bought by a Cambodian family who'd transformed it. The café was housed in one of a row of 1930s buildings, ornate plasterwork above modern frontages. We sat in orange plastic chairs at immaculate formica tables, and I asked Todd what had brought him back to Tawanui.

'To the teeming metropolis?' he asked, smiling. 'A few things came together. Dad's got emphysema. You know what an ailing parent involves.'

'I do now.'

'I was driving back and forth from Wellington. My sister's here, and I'm pretty close to her children, so that's another drawcard. I was feeling burned out professionally. And then my long-term partner and I split up. Not my choice. We'd been together ten years, we owned a house and a beautiful dog called Elsa, who I had to leave behind. Not much fun.'

'I'm sorry,' I said. 'Ten years is a long time.'

'Mm, and Wellington's a lot smaller than you'd think. I seemed to bump into Stephen constantly. So . . . a great moment to make life changes.'

He broke off to thank Chouma, the café's owner, as she brought our coffee. I was intrigued by what I'd just heard—and maybe a *little* disappointed. I hadn't expected a Stephen, ex or otherwise.

'Anyway,' he continued, 'Tawanui has welcomed me home, apart from two clients who took their business away because I'm an abomination before God. I'm old enough to accept being a provincial lawyer in a backwater. The payoff is more time for flying.' He hesitated, pouring water into both our glasses. 'My day began with a call from your brother.'

'Oh dear.'

'Not a happy bunny. He's talking about professional misconduct.'

I began to splutter apologies. Todd waved them away, assuring me that he had broad shoulders.

'I'm sure you have,' I said, with a glance at his shoulders, 'but what a bloody insult!'

'Money destroys families. You know, it's a funny thing: nine times out of ten, as a lawyer, I find all the fuss and rage isn't really about the money. It's about other stuff.'

He launched into an explanation of the documents he'd drawn up and would send along to Dad's bank. While he was talking, another customer caught my attention. A tall guy, angular, with a frill of hair like a monk's tonsure. I jerked my chin towards him as he left the café.

'Vince Price?' I mouthed.

'That's Vince.'

'Does he still talk about alien abductions?'

'Yep.' Todd sighed. 'Leah went up in a spaceship.'

We watched through the window as Vince hurried away down the main street, carrying an award-winning pie in a paper bag.

'How long were you and Leah together?' I asked.

'Actually'—Todd was balancing a teaspoon on his finger, like a seesaw—'we never were. That was a complete fiction.'

'*What?*'

'Being an item with Leah made me look straight. It suited her, too, because people like your brother were always bothering her.'

'Friends *without* benefits!' I was chuckling, bemused. 'Whose idea was this?'

'Hers. Leah was a good friend. She thought I should just come out, but I didn't have the courage. You might think Tawanui is conservative nowadays, but remember what it was like back then? While I was at school, homosexual acts between men were still illegal.'

'In the 1980s? You're kidding me!'

'It's true,' he said. 'The law wasn't changed until 1986. Leah thought it was hilarious to be my pretend girlfriend. We used to park my car in romantic spots, knowing people would see it, and sit there reading books or playing cards. Then we'd reappear looking dishevelled, buttons undone, and put up with all the grubby remarks. Leah liked fooling people.'

'Did she? I didn't know that about her.'

Nothing is as it seems. Truth and lies are crumpled up together; you can't tell where one ends and the other begins.

Todd's smile had faded. 'Here's the thing,' he said, laying down the spoon. 'Remember there was a rumour about Leah having bruises? Well, she did. I saw her in a bar in Wellington, I think it was the February before she disappeared. She had a black eye and lots of bruising here.' He laid his fingers on his own lower arm. 'Said she'd been knocked down some steps on

Lambton Quay—someone was running and barged into her by accident. She was laughing about this poor young guy: jug ears, twitching nose, wouldn't stop apologising. She said he reminded her of the White Rabbit in *Alice in Wonderland*.'

'Did you believe her?'

Todd nodded unhappily. 'At the time. It rang true. She wasn't the kind of woman you'd associate with being a victim, was she? I mean, *you* knew her, she was always in and out of your house. She was tough. Sharp. Not scared of anyone. Some people found her a bit arrogant, but I think that was just a part she played, so they wouldn't pity her. You know, the girl whose father was dying inch by inch. That day in Wellington was the last time I ever saw her, though, and I still wonder. She wasn't her usual self.'

'In what way?'

'A bit flat, a bit . . .' He screwed up his face. 'I want to say nervy, but that's not quite right. She talked about deadlines for collecting data, applying for a research grant from the Department of Conservation, teaching undergraduates . . . lots of other work—I can't remember now.'

'Did you tell the police about these injuries?'

'I did.'

'And?'

'People had already reported them. They didn't think it was significant, and they were probably right. But when I wake up at four in the morning—which is pretty often—I wonder whether that shove down the steps wasn't accidental. Maybe she was in trouble. I start thinking about the hiker on Biddulph Road in the early morning. Remember? In the blue or green beanie. Never came forward. I mean, who on earth *was* that?'

I was taken aback. I didn't have Todd down as the kind of guy who'd lie awake at night, torturing himself with decades-old guilt. He took a sip of coffee, clearing his throat before he spoke again.

'Leah and I were born within three weeks of one another, in the old maternity unit in Jellicoe Street. We went to the same play-group, the same schools, the same swimming lessons, the same university. I'd known her all my life—literally, *all* my life. But I failed her that day. I scurried back to my office and got on with some world-shatteringly banal task—probably helping somebody to screw over their employee. I meant to give her a call sometime. I never got around to it, and then it was too late.'

'Is this why you keep flying around in the ranges—out of guilt?'

He shrugged, but he didn't deny it.

'Where is she?' he asked. 'Where the hell *is* she? We know she stayed in Biddulph's bivvy on the Friday night, because she left that note. What happened to her?'

He'd run out of breath, eyes reddening behind his glasses.

'Look, Todd'—I tapped the table in front of him—'I was the last person to speak to Leah, and I'm telling you she was fine. No bruises, no sinister mobsters tailing her. Tramping in the ranges can be risky at the best of times. Tramping alone, in winter, in brutal weather? More than risky.'

'I know.'

'Nothing you did would have changed what happened.'

We left the café soon after that and began to wander back towards Dad's car. I'd parked outside the Anglican church, with its cream-painted weatherboards, red tin roof and tiny wooden belfry. This was the scene of Manu's funeral, Carmen's wedding, Leah's memorial service.

'Stephen said I was obsessed,' said Todd, as we reached the car. 'He used to accuse me of being hung up on an invisible woman. Neither true nor fair.'

We spent a happy interlude leaning against the bonnet, bitching about our exes. That's always fun. We had to call a halt when my phone rang. It was Dad, worrying about where I'd got to. Todd politely engrossed himself in the church noticeboard while I tried to reassure him.

'I'm in town, Dad. With Todd. The solicitor, you know? I'll be right back! Twenty minutes. Get the kettle on. Twenty minutes. Twenty minutes, okay?'

'Sounds as though your bail's been revoked,' said Todd, as I shoved my phone back into my pocket.

He was still looking at the board. It was bright with posters and notices: a jumble sale, a parent-and-toddler group, a school play, the times of services.

'I can't walk past this place without thinking about Leah's memorial service,' he said. 'Remember that day?'

Oh yes. I remembered that day.

•

November 1994

As we gather at the church, a cloud-wave is breaking all along the Ruahines, blown by gales on the western side. It looks like a tsunami rushing to meet us, destroying everything in its path. Seems apt on such a day.

Leah is gone. She's been gone five months, yet she isn't officially dead. She's a missing person. The police haven't closed her file, but they're satisfied that she died accidentally in the ranges. Her room in the Wellington flat has been re-let, her research and teaching work reallocated. Her possessions have all been packed up by friends—what an awful job to have to do—before being returned to Raewyn. I came across the boxes and bags piled in Leah's bedroom and found myself touching them, feeling as though they were soaked in her spirit. Her mustard yellow car has been released to the family. It's rusting away now, parked in the long grass behind the chicken shed. Her lip salve, sunscreen, a packet of mints are still in the glove box. I've seen Ira sitting in the passenger seat, his head turned as though he's talking to an invisible driver.

There's no body, no explanation, nothing to mourn. There is only her absence.

It's the vicar who suggested a memorial service. He buried Manu. He felt it might help everyone to have a ceremony of some kind: an acknowledgement of Leah's life, of her family's agony, of the community's horror.

Almost four hundred people have turned up to rally around Raewyn and Ira. The little church is overflowing, the service relayed through a closed-circuit system to a marquee outside. There are colleagues and friends from Victoria University, a delegation from the Department of Conservation, throngs of ex-pupils and teachers from Tawanui High. I've postponed my flight to Ecuador, but I'll be leaving in a couple of days. I'm all packed.

I keep thinking about the story of Tom Sawyer and his friends, who made an entrance at their own memorial service. Perhaps the double doors at the back of St John's will be flung open dramatically to reveal Leah, silhouetted against the setting sun. I imagine the gasps, the cries of joy, the church bells pealing in celebration.

But no. This is not a day for miracles. Raewyn and Ira sit in the front pew with family around them. Raewyn somehow manages to smile as she speaks to well-wishers. Ira hunches like an angry prize-fighter, his eyebrows drawn together, as if by sheer rage he might force the universe to return his sister to him.

I watch from two rows back as Brad Taylor approaches him, laying a hand on his shoulder and speaking briefly. I've not seen Brad since I woke up in his bedroom that day. As he walks away from Ira he meets my eye, mouths, *Hi*. We both pull sad little grimace-smiles. While we were partying, Leah may have been spending her last night alive.

Carmen darts into our pew just before the service begins.

'I'm fucking livid,' she hisses out of the corner of her mouth. 'People are such bastards. Someone just tried to tell me Leah was pregnant!'

I gawp at her. 'Says who?'

She shakes her head, mopping mascara from under her eyes with a tissue. 'People with big mouths and no brains, putting two and two together, making fifty. Some nosy housemate decided she had morning sickness, 'cos she was in the bathroom a while and came out looking peaky. People saying she stuck to orange juice at my wedding, wore that baggy lace dress . . . I mean so what? She looked gorgeous in that dress!'

'Sounds like typical Tawanui bullshit.'

'Too right. Why would she take risks with the weather, if she knew she was pregnant? God, people in this town are so—'

The vicar is welcoming us all to St John's, *for this celebration of the life of an extraordinary woman.*

So many people want to give tributes. Friends, relatives, students. A university professor talks about how she was a *taonga* of the nation, a treasure. Eddie is sitting beside me. I've hardly spoken to him since he tried to trash my shop at the petrol station, but I soften a bit when I realise he's in floods of tears.

'This isn't happening,' he croaks, as Carmen reaches across me to give him a tissue. 'Tell me this isn't happening. How can this be happening?'

In the silence after the final blessing, a lone bagpiper strikes up a lament. He's one of Leah's teachers from Tawanui High. A minute later the skirling is overlaid by Ira shouting, screaming, and the rhythmic, ground-shaking stamping of feet as he leads a crowd of relatives and friends in a haka. The two strands are a tribute to Leah's Scottish and Māori heritage. I'd known it was planned, but that discordant blending, mingled with the sobs of a bewildered community, is the most haunting sound I have ever heard. It overwhelms the wooden building and everyone within it, including me. I know I'll never forget it.

Now that Leah is gone, I remember her showing Ira and me how to make toffee, both of us standing on rickety chairs at the cooker. *Drop it into the cold water, see if it's ready, yum!* Now that she's gone, I remember her rescuing me when some bullying kids on the bus were trying to throw my bag out of the window. Now that she's gone, I treasure the warmth of her last smile. *Ecuador! Good for you, Emily.* I find myself reaching for Carmen's tissues too.

When we file outside, Raewyn is standing alone in a milling crowd. I think she's been waiting for Dad, because she immediately approaches us.

'Where is she, Felix?' she asks. 'I wish I knew where she is. I just want to bring her home.'

As he tries to answer, his voice gives out. He presses his fist to his mouth, closes his eyes. For an awful moment I think he's going to break down. He swallows hard before gesturing up towards the ranges.

'She *is* home,' he whispers.

Raewyn's gaze follows his. 'She'd rather be up there than buried in this churchyard, wouldn't she? But I expected to be sitting in the front pew when she got married! Not this.' Raewyn reaches out, fumbling blindly, until she catches hold of Dad's hand. 'Not this, Felix. Not this, not this. Dear God, not this.'

He covers her hand with his other one. Dad, who never touches anyone unless they're his patient.

They stand like that, holding hands. It's a strange sight, but then this whole day has been surreal. It seems as though they are both Leah's parents.

FIFTEEN

March 2019

The early-morning air began to snap with a hint of autumn. I welcomed the cooler nights, and it was generally warm again by ten o'clock when we had coffee on the porch.

Morning was still our happiest time, when Dad was least frightened and least frightening. He showed a great interest in Nathan. Sometimes we'd have a video call with Indonesia, or I'd show him the latest photos. More often, though, he and I just chatted. His earliest memories were the clearest. He was especially lucid when raging about Maggie Thatcher, the poll tax, Arthur Scargill and the miners' strike. We used to put the world to rights, he and I.

Once, while we were playing chess, we stopped to watch Ira and his dogs moving a mob of sheep. My friend worked all day, every day, beginning at first light. When I remarked on this, Dad nodded.

'His father was the same. A job list as long as your arm, but always time to spare for other people.'

'I hardly remember Manu back then,' I said. 'When he was still fit and well.'

He moved a pawn, capturing one of mine.

'The day we moved into this house, he and Raewyn came round to welcome us, bringing vegetables from their garden. We were having trouble with the pump, so Manu immediately fetched his toolbox and fixed it.' He frowned as I took his pawn with my knight. 'Did you *really* mean to do that, Emily? Righto. If you insist.'

And my hapless knight joined the lengthening row of his prisoners.

'Manu,' I prompted him. 'Did you notice something was wrong?'

'I didn't. I probably should have. But when a man works so hard, you assume that's why he seems a bit haggard.' Dad looked anxious, glancing at Ira's distant figure. 'He came to see me in the surgery. He'd got himself all dressed in his tidy clothes, said he was sorry to bother me, he was sure he was wasting my time, but . . . something wasn't quite right. In fact, he'd felt "not quite right" for years. It was getting worse. He'd been making mistakes, had become increasingly clumsy and quick to anger— something he despised in himself. What worried him was that his grandmother and at least one uncle had begun rather like this, and they ended up in a terrible state. He described how they rolled on the floor, they stretched their limbs, they twisted their bodies into strange postures and, above all, they never stopped moving. Some kind of wasting disease, he thought, but nobody knew what. They ended up bedridden for years. Much worse than bedridden, worse . . .'

Dad didn't finish the sentence. I thought he'd drifted away from our conversation, but he hadn't.

'The way his relatives had lived and died was of grave concern to me. His father died of a heart condition in early middle age, but Manu now suspected that he too was showing early symptoms. It all rang a bell, reminded me of a case I'd seen in Leeds. I examined

Manu and didn't at all like what I saw. Telltale signs were there, if you knew what to look for. He was about ten years older than Raewyn, late forties, but of course his children were still quite young. I referred him urgently to a specialist and one awful—*awful*—day I had to go and break the news.'

'They must have been shattered.'

'Dear Raewyn. Oh, dear Raewyn. She took one look at my face and insisted on putting out afternoon tea. Then she sat and held Manu's hand. I remember that especially; I was struck by it. She wouldn't let go of his hand, or perhaps he wouldn't let go of hers. I had to explain to them about Huntington's, that we were dealing with a degenerative neurological disease. Incurable, ultimately fatal. They had questions. How long did he have? Could anything be done? Manu called it a "one-way ticket", and he was right. I had to confirm their fear that it's genetic. Scientists hadn't isolated the exact gene at that time, but we knew there was a significant risk of their children going the same'—his voice caught for a moment; tears were brimming—'of going the same way. Oh dear.' He swallowed, wiping his eyes with his thumb. 'I've seen Huntington's described as a combination of Alzheimer's, Parkinson's and motor neurone disease. Beyond cruel.'

'Did you tell them all this?'

'They knew. They'd seen it before, seen the destruction it wreaks. I tried to temper my news with hope: that medical science was constantly advancing, that progression is generally slow. Manu might have decades more, perhaps long enough to see his children grow up—though they wouldn't all be good years. I recall Raewyn saying, *Well, we'll just have to roll our sleeves up and get on with it!*'

'And they did.'

'They did. They were both pioneers in their way. Raewyn's ancestors were Scottish whalers, did you know that? One of them survived two shipwrecks! Manu's father cleared and fenced this land. After the diagnosis, Manu carried on farming for as long as he could. Raewyn helped him, and drove her bus—though by the end she was caring for him twenty-four hours a day.'

'Amazing people.'

'Mm.' Dad was chewing one corner of his mouth. 'I once found her watching him through the window. He was trying to wheel a barrow of logs from the woodshed to the house. The barrow kept tipping over. He'd laboriously pile the wood back in—all his limbs up, down, everywhere, the involuntary movements—then a few more steps and over it would go again.' Dad was demonstrating with his hands, over and over, a tipping wheelbarrow. 'Bellows of frustration! Raewyn was beside herself. *He's so stubborn, Felix, he's so bloody stubborn, that man. He won't let me help, but he gets so angry!* Next time the barrow tipped, Manu fell too, and lay with his arms and legs flailing. I could have wept. I knew it was only the beginning for my friends. They suffered that cat-and-mouse disease—years of it—down, down, down. Each time he deteriorated the whole family would roll up their sleeves again, they'd make the best of it. Then *down* he'd go again. And of course his personality and intellect changed beyond recognition. She lost him long before he died.'

I'd never had this kind of conversation with Dad before. It was all new, this honesty about his emotional life. I couldn't even remember him describing someone as a friend.

'Manu had a sense of purpose,' he said at last, picking up his queen. 'His mission was to farm this land, to bring up his children. The disease robbed him of his ability to fulfil that purpose. It robbed him of all that he was. It took tremendous spirit not to despair. That's the real enemy. Despair.'

He moved his queen along the diagonal track until she was completely surrounded by her enemies. His fingers rested lightly on her crown as he checked his new position.

'I never got the hang of it,' I said.

'Chess? Or despair?'

'Purpose. I think I've missed mine altogether.'

'I'm sure you haven't.'

It was my turn to show a bit of honesty.

'C'mon, Dad. I'm forty-seven this year, a single parent with a long and unedifying string of failed relationships behind me. My only asset is a flat in Brent Cross, above a drycleaners, which mostly belongs to Barclay's Bank. Do I save lives? No! Do I motivate millions to strike for the climate? Nope! I'm a freeloader in this world, a consumer, a polluter. I don't catch the ball of life and run with it. I duck while it whizzes past my head.'

'Not so!' Dad looked quite distressed. 'What about your wonderful picture books?'

'Hmm.'

'And you have a . . . erm, now . . .' He waggled his fingers in the air. He was trying so very hard to remember. 'I think . . . am I right . . . you have children?'

'Just the one. Nathan.'

'Who?'

'Nathan. My son.'

'Of course!' He lit up. 'Yes, I know Nathan! Terrific young man.'

'He *is* terrific. He's funny, he's kind—a wise head on young shoulders. But that's not my achievement, is it? That's all down to him. I look at you, I hear how everyone around here has a heroic story about you.'

'I'm not at all what they think.'

His smile had drained away. He seemed to shrink before my eyes, his hands clasped between his knees. Ten, maybe twenty seconds passed in silence. I was afraid he might be having a stroke.

'You okay?' I asked. 'Hello, Dad? You okay?'

He blinked rapidly, and then he was back. 'I think it's your turn,' he announced, gesturing at our game. 'And I'm afraid you're about to lose quite catastrophically. Come on now, stop stalling.'

Sure enough, four moves later he had checkmate.

•

That night, a wail jerked me out of a dream. My first thought was of the ghost of Hilary Izzard.

There it was again: high-pitched keening, like a lost child.

I was out of bed and flicking on lights, thinking about the quickest way to get hold of a vet. I'd roasted a chicken for dinner. Maybe one of the dogs had fished a bone out of the bin and was dying of peritonitis?

But there was no need for a vet. The dogs had made themselves comfy on the sofa in the snug. Both were awake, listening to the cries.

'Hey,' I whispered, tapping Dad's door as I looked in. 'You all right?'

His lamp was on. He was sitting on the side of his bed in his pyjamas and leather slippers, his cheeks flushed. He turned his gaze onto me—wildly, uncomprehendingly.

'I want to go home,' he said.

'You *are* home.'

'Thank you for having me, but I must be going now. I have things to do. Please help me.'

He'd stood up while he talked, and was pulling a sweater on over his pyjamas: inside out, back to front.

'Where are my car keys? I really do have to get home. Please, please help me.'

'This is your home, Dad. I promise you.'

'This place? What on earth are you talking about—do you think I'm stupid? This is *not* my home.' He began a frantic search all around the room, his voice rising. I heard his terror. 'Where have you hidden my car keys? Who are you? Are you a doctor?'

'It's me,' I said, reaching out to take his arm. 'It's Emily.'

He jerked his arm from my grasp and lashed out, knocking me away. I was caught off guard—staggered, tripped, ended up sitting heavily on the bed. My cultured, too-reserved father had been possessed by a crazed creature. He reminded me of a feral cat I once rescued from a drain. It spat and yowled, tore gouges in my arm while I saved its life.

'You've got no bloody right to keep me here,' he screamed, while I made a break for the door. 'You evil person. I am *going* now. I demand that you give me my car keys! Give me my car keys! Where am I?'

He was still shrieking when I burst back into the kitchen, almost in tears. He'd lived in this house for forty years. How could he believe I was a wicked abductor? I put on shoes and a jacket and stood by the outside door, ready to bolt if he really became violent. His keys were hanging on a nail in the carport. Perhaps I should drive up to Ira's cottage right now and ask for help?

Gyp was trotting around the kitchen, obviously upset by all the noise. Gloria came and nuzzled my hand as though trying to comfort me. I was so grateful to her.

'What's happened to him, Gloria?' I moaned. 'Where's he gone?'

And then, quite suddenly, the shouting stopped.

Five minutes. Ten minutes. Silence.

The grandmother clock was striking half past two when I tapped on his door again, a mug of tea in my hand. A peace offering. He was sitting on his bed, in much the same position as before. Slippers, pyjamas. Deep bags under his eyes.

This time, though, he looked around with a weary smile. 'Ah! Good morning.'

Two thirty.

'Morning, Dad.'

'Is that tea? Thank you! I was just thinking how nice some tea would be. How did you know?'

'Lucky guess,' I said, setting the mug down on the steel trunk he used as a bedside table. 'I don't think it's quite time to be getting up. How about you get back into bed?'

He swung his legs up, laid his head on the pillow. No anger now, only childlike obedience. I drew the covers over him, took his hot-water bottle along to the kitchen and refilled it from the kettle. By the time I brought it back, he was drowsy.

'Oh, lovely,' he said. 'How very kind. But how about you? When does your shift finish?'

'Not until morning.'

I stood near his bed for a moment, not wanting to leave him alone.

'Listen,' he whispered. 'There's a morepork.'

And so there was. Such magic. A mysterious little owl, a creature from another world, calling in the frozen stillness, *morr-porr, morr-porr*. The cry made me shiver.

'Hine-ruru,' said Dad. 'The owl woman. Someone once told me she's a guardian spirit, who guides people.'

I stepped across to the window, pressing my face close to the glass. Inky blackness, no moon, no stars. The owl was still calling. She sounded kind. Perhaps she could guide me.

We didn't do goodnight kisses, never had; but as I turned away from the window, he held out his hand to me.

I squeezed his fingers. 'Night, Dad.'

'Goodnight.'

SIXTEEN

Dad was already up and about when I woke the next morning. I didn't want to join him. Not yet. The events of the night had shaken me.

I heard his footsteps in the kitchen. I think he was listening to the BBC World Service, and I caught the word *Brexit*. When the sliding door squeaked, I looked out in time to spot him marching across the paddock in the direction of Raewyn's house, Gyp and Gloria zigzagging around him. He looked spry, with a spring in his step. Daylight had chased away the stranger in his mirror.

He often paid a morning visit to Raewyn; she'd probably give him breakfast. I waited half an hour and then phoned, just to be sure.

'Yes, he's in my kitchen,' she said cheerfully. 'We're cooking pancakes and bacon.'

'We had a frightening time last night,' I told her. 'I didn't know what to do.'

The floodgates opened, and I poured out every horrible detail. Raewyn listened to the whole story, murmuring her sympathy.

'One day he won't come back, will he?' I asked. My voice was wobbling. 'He'll be trapped in his hell forever.'

'Maybe. But you're doing wonderfully right now, Emily. Hold on to that.'

'I don't think I am.'

'Tell you what,' she suggested, after a moment's thought. 'I'm delivering meals on wheels today, and I could do with some help. Shall I ask Felix to come with me? I'll bring him home sometime this afternoon.'

She wouldn't let me thank her.

'Your dad and I go back a long way,' she said. 'We're friends. You get on with your work and don't worry about him.'

I really did need to make some progress, because by tonight I was scheduled to email the mock-up layout of *Christmas Kitten* to my editor, who would run it by her design team and Sarah. Hours passed as I worked away, downing cups of coffee, eating a quick sandwich at my table, humming along to music on the radio. I found inspiration in hundreds of photos of Max, my tabby friend in London. Dear old Max. I wished he were sleeping beside me now.

In the late afternoon, Gyp arrived home by himself, butting the studio door open with his head before hurtling in. I wasn't surprised to see him. He knew his way to and from Raewyn's house.

'Had a good day?' I asked, scratching him under the chin. 'Caught any rabbits? Nope, thought not.'

Within minutes he was fussing about rats again. It's impossible to concentrate when a silly little dog is charging around your studio, barking and scratching at the carpet. I jumped crossly to my feet, shoving my pencil behind my ear.

'Give it a rest, will you?' I scolded. 'Bloody dog! I haven't got time for you and your neuroses.'

I found him in Carmen's wardrobe, trying to shove his nose through a crack in the floor. I imagined a family of rats rolling around with glee under there, slapping their rodent knees. Beatrix Potter would have written a whole book about it.

The hanging space in the wardrobe was empty, but the shelves were stacked with clothes and shoes and other detritus left by Carmen and Mum: a lamp, a set of electric rollers that belonged in the 1980s, Carmen's riding hat, a cheap print of a ballet dancer. It all smelled fusty. I'd already looked in here a couple of times, wondering whether I should have a proper sort-out. Someone would have to, one day.

'You'll never squeeze down that hole. Daft animal,' I muttered, idly picking up the riding helmet and trying it on my own head. I pulled out Carmen's jodhpurs, unfolded them, gave them a shake. Teensy-weensy little things!

'How the hell did she manage to fit into these?' I asked Gyp. 'My bottom hasn't been this size since I was ten years old.'

I spotted a dash of colour, a cloth of some kind, peeking from under a tangle of belts. Casually, still burbling away to the dog, I reached to tug it out. For a long moment I stood with a riding hat on my head, moth-eaten jodhpurs slung over my shoulder.

And a turquoise beanie in my hand.

She was twirling it around. She was pulling it onto her head, a splash of brilliance in the gloom and rain. Nobody ever saw her again.

The world fell away. I forgot about Gyp, about the Christmas kitten. I carried my find to the window, holding it up to the light.

I was looking at a simple dome, stitched from four pieces and designed for functionality rather than fashion. According to the label it was *100% merino wool. Made in New Zealand*. It smelled of damp, and a constellation of small holes had turned one edge into lace. Moths. It could well be twenty-five years old. Strands of hair, long and curled and easily as dark as Leah's, had caught on an inside seam. There was no doubt about it: this hat in my hands was the spitting image of one that haunted my memories. I could see it so clearly, twirling around on her finger.

And then I recalled the note in my father's diary:

LEAH LEAH
REMEMBER!

'Remember what, Dad?' I whispered.

The double rumble of the cattle grid—and the sight of Raewyn's car rounding the corner of the house—set my heart pounding. I moved fast, stashing the beanie at the back of the cupboard before hurrying to meet them.

Dad was already on his way up the porch steps, clutching a cardboard box to his chest. It was stacked high with lettuce, capsicum, beans and other vegetables I didn't even recognise.

'Hello there,' he said. 'These are for us.'

'I'm dumping half my veggie patch on you people,' added Raewyn.

I thought about my deadline. I really ought to get back to work, but my mind was overflowing. I felt as though there were a neon sign flashing above my head, a thought bubble in hysterically screaming capitals: *TURQUOISE BEANIE! CARMEN'S WARDROBE!*

'Half your vegetable patch,' I said, trying to sound jolly, 'calls for a glass of wine.'

Dad looked dog-tired. He thanked Raewyn for the vegetables and the lift home, before making an escape to the study. Raewyn and I sat on the porch with a bottle of sauvignon. She was wearing baggy jeans rolled up to mid-calf, her hair loose and wispy.

Bright, bright turquoise. Twirling it on her finger.

Strands of cloud had wrapped themselves around the peaks, thin and inconsequential, like broken cobwebs. Raewyn looked up at the early evening sky and said she hoped we might have some rain soon, for the sake of the farmers. We needed the grass to grow before the first frosts, because ... and she'd seen Ira earlier, he had two bulls with some kind of infection, he was giving them antibiotics, and ...

The more wine I downed, the better I felt about that beanie. What a fuss about nothing! I was being bloody ridiculous. How could something Leah was wearing when she disappeared possibly have ended up in this house? I might as well go full Vince Price and decide she was abducted by aliens. There must be hundreds of overpriced merino caps like this one all over the country. It could have belonged to Mum, Carmen—any visitor over the decades. I couldn't even be sure it was the same turquoise as Leah's. I'm an artist, I like to think I've an eye for colour, but it was beyond arrogant to rely on my memory of the precise shade of a scrap of fabric glimpsed a quarter of a century ago. As for those dark strands of hair—so what? They weren't evidence of anything at all.

'I'll tell you something,' said Raewyn. 'I'm sure Ira's got a girlfriend.'

This was gossip-worthy enough to distract me. Since our conversation on his front deck, when he hinted there might be somebody new in his life, Ira had completely clammed up.

Raewyn filled me in on her detective work. She'd spotted a ute coming and going up the track to his place: a white Ford Ranger, driven by a woman. Of course, asking Ira about this mysterious visitor was a waste of breath.

'Like pulling teeth,' she declared. 'I wondered whether she might be a stock agent or something, but it's a very determined stock agent who turns up at six at night and stays until six the next morning.'

'All night!'

'All night. And this afternoon I saw that same ute parked outside the primary school. She was getting in, with two children.'

'What does she look like?'

'Jeans, gumboots. *Very* curly hair'—Raewyn chuckled, demonstrating a kind of hair firework with her hands—'and those kids were obviously hers, because their hair was exactly the same. Quite comical, really.'

'Ira's kind of age?'

'It's hard to tell nowadays.' Raewyn held up her crossed fingers. 'I just so, *so* hope he can find happiness.'

I reached for the wine bottle. Raewyn put a hand over her glass, but I sloshed a generous top-up into my own. Sod it. I wasn't going to meet today's deadline now. First thing tomorrow would have to do.

'And how are you getting on?' asked Raewyn. 'Happier than you were this morning?'

'I'm okay, thanks to you.'

Our neighbour could have passed for a much younger woman. Only the backs of her hands gave away her age. They were mottled with freckles and raised, rough patches, the result of decades of gardening in the Hawke's Bay sun. Dr Ellis had frozen the worst of them away more than once, lest they develop into skin cancer. Raewyn still wore both her wedding and engagement rings, their gold bands worn thin from years of life and love. I wondered whether they'd ever been removed, since the day Manu put them on her finger.

She reached to squeeze my hand in hers.

'Well,' she said. 'If you're ever *not* okay, you know where I am.'

Forget it, I told myself. *It's just a stupid hat.*

SEVENTEEN

'March has marched away,' mused Dad, crossing off days on his Yorkshire Dales calendar. 'Where do the weeks go?'

I was wondering the same thing myself. A fortnight had passed since I'd found the beanie in the cupboard, and I hadn't taken it out again. If I didn't look at it, I could almost forget about it.

Dad settled down in his armchair in the study with a book on his lap, a biscuit at his elbow. Both were window-dressing. The biscuit wouldn't be touched, and he'd be nodding off any minute. I was tempted to do the same, because I'd got up at five for a video call with the design team. Instead, I made myself a cup of super-strong coffee and got back to work. I was experimenting with tiny images of cats leaping across the letters on the title page. It kept the shadows at bay, to be doing something I understood and could control.

An orchestral suite was playing on the radio, which suited me because I work best when listening to music without words. From time to time I stepped back from the table to conduct an imaginary orchestra with both arms, using my sketching pencil as a baton. At times like this I forgot where I was; I almost forgot *who* I was. It was like a trance. I'd slipped into a state of complete immersion when unearthly howls from the study had me pelting down the corridor.

Dad was bent double, his expression like nothing I'd ever seen on any human being. His mouth was open in a scream, strings of spit between his lips. Tears coursed down his face. I thought he was in agony.

'It's my writing!' He was winded, gasping for breath. 'My writing, my writing, my . . . God help me! It was on my notice-board. Why the heck would I write this?'

He had some sheets of paper in his hand. The top one was covered in red sharpie pen.

FELIX, YOU HAVE ALZHEIMER'S
THIS IS TRUE
Read the attached report

'Come with me,' I ordered, taking the awful thing from him and hiding it under a pile of medical journals. 'Into the garden. C'mon. I'd like to see the roses! Please can you show me?'

He didn't protest as I grabbed his arm and steered him out of the room. He stumbled along the corridor, still sobbing, out through the kitchen doors and into the sunshine. I was acting on instinct, but to my relief the strategy seemed to work. After a few minutes in the autumnal brightness and birdsong, he began to forget his terror. Short-term memory loss isn't all bad.

We pottered at a snail's pace across the lawn, heading for the roses he'd planted and lovingly tended for years. The drought had taken a toll. Leaves were curled, suffering from some kind of fungus, but there were still some healthy blooms.

Dad leaned down, taking a flower in one hand as he inhaled its scent. 'A damask,' he said.

'Heavenly.'

'Do you like roses? I'll cut this one for you later, to take home with you.'

As we walked on, he began to make polite conversation.

'I grow a number of varieties. It's a foolish hobby, with this climate. We have frosts in winter, dry summers which stress them. I think you're from Britain? Mm.' Nodding. 'I can tell from your accent. So am I! A Yorkshire lad, though you might not guess. See this here?' He'd stopped beside the pergola, where a bush had managed to produce a spray of yellow blooms. 'I planted this banksia in the year we arrived in Tawanui. My wife, Lillian, wanted a pergola with a seat and a view of the ranges. And she got one, as you can see. But I'm afraid it wasn't enough to make her happy.'

'I'm sure she was happy sometimes.'

'She didn't want to be here. Went back to Yorkshire in the end, and I quite understood. I was a lousy husband, I'm afraid. I'd wasted enough of her life. We were fundamentally unsuited.'

'You think so?'

'Oh yes! Fundamentally. Nothing in common. We married far, *far* too young, at a time when I was grieving for my sister.' He glanced at me. 'My sister Helen. She died at the age of eighteen, did you know? Lillian was a sunny, laughing girl back then. She kept my grief at bay—that was the attraction. I was a medical student, and Lillian thought she was getting a dashing young doctor. Oh dear, she was terribly disappointed. She used to complain that I had no warmth, I'm robotic. She said I had frozen her happiness. She was a good-time girl.'

'Oi!' I cried, with mock indignation. 'That's my mother you're talking about!'

'*Your* mother? No, no, I don't think so. I don't think . . .'

He sank onto the wooden seat in the shade of the pergola. I sat beside him.

'I wish I were a robot,' he whispered. 'I have tried to be.'

'Why?'

'Better all round.'

I crushed a leggy sprig of lavender in my hand, holding the crumpled flowers to my face. It smelled of childhood, of croquet on the lawn, playing in a rubber-tyre swing with Ira, swimming trips to the river—Dad with a towel over one shoulder, wearing his sunhat. Yells of laughter, diamonds of flashing sunlight, that euphoric shock of cold as we hurled ourselves into the current.

These were false memories, or at least heavily censored. Lavender-scented, with undernotes that weren't so sweet: my mother's loneliness, my father's remoteness, Manu's inexorable deterioration. What else was hidden beneath the surface?

Before we jumped into the deeper pools, Ira and I always made sure to splash loudly, so that any freshwater eels would take the hint and disappear. It was best not to startle them. When we were eleven or so, we befriended a massive blue-grey creature, whose snout would break the surface as she accepted our offerings of dog food. We made a pet of her—or she of us, I was never quite sure which. She was at least a metre long, and spent her days in a dark spot under the overhang of the bank. Ira named her Kikorangi, which he said means Sky Blue. I protested that she wasn't sky blue at all, but he didn't care.

One day, we invited Leah to come and meet our eel. She always showed an interest in the bugs and butterflies we found. She strode beside us across the farm in her denim shorts, carrying a bag of leftovers from the Judo Club sausage sizzle fundraiser. Even then, at sixteen, she was a walking encyclopedia when it came to natural history. We three lay on our stomachs on the edge of the bank above Kikorangi's pool, hand-feeding sausages to a sinuous shadow. I remember how chuffed Ira and I both were, because his clever sister seemed fascinated by our pet.

'A longfin eel. Your beautiful *tuna* will have been born way, way out in the Pacific, maybe as far as Tonga. Nobody knows for sure,' she told us. 'She was tiny then, but she floated on the ocean currents, thousands of kilometres, all the way to the coast of New Zealand. Then she became a little glass eel, and she somehow swam up the rivers until she came to this spot and made it her home. It's a privilege to have her—and she has enough dangers to worry about, so don't you let your friends trap and kill her.'

Leah dangled a sausage under the water, laughing with real delight as the eel took it from her hand.

'One day, maybe when you two have jobs and kids of your own, Kikorangi will leave here.'

'Why?' Ira looked a bit hurt. 'She should stay.'

'She'll change again. Her eyes will turn blue, like her name, and her body will get ready, and then she'll set out. This time she'll be going the other way—back down the rivers, across the ocean, all the way to the place she was born. It'll be her last journey. She'll spawn way out there, in the Pacific, and then she'll die. Her life's work will have been done. By then she might be sixty, even a hundred years old.'

'So she'll live longer than Dad,' said Ira.

Leah touched his cheek with her knuckle. 'I think so, bud. Sorry.'

'How will she know when it's time to set off?' I asked. 'How will she know the way back to Tonga, or wherever it is she goes?'

'That,' said Leah, 'is one of those mysteries that not even David Attenborough understands. But she will know, and she will go. Nature's full of secrets. I want to find some of the answers. That will be *my* life's work.'

•

'You know, I have this awful feeling,' Dad said quietly, as we sat in the pergola. 'This *awful* feeling. I think something terrible has just happened. I'm appallingly frightened of something.'

'What kind of thing?'

'Something in the study. I feel sure there's a monster in my study. Should we go and look?'

Reaching for his hand, I tipped the crushed lavender flowers into the palm. I hoped the scent might lighten his mood.

'Something evil,' he whispered, pressing his nose into the lavender.

The dogs wandered out of the house and came to lie on the prickly grass at our feet. A breeze stirred, brushing against my face and lifting Dad's hair. The weather was changing, a cloud tsunami rearing over the mountains. I could feel the dropping pressure.

'I'm so sorry,' said Dad.

'Why would you be sorry?'

'I didn't bring her home. Broke her mother's heart.'

I knew who he was talking about.

'You searched and searched,' I said. 'You couldn't have done more.'

No answer. Soon he was asleep, a frown creasing his forehead, head lolling against the back of the seat. It reminded me of times when two-year-old Nathan dropped off in mid-tantrum, curled up on the sofa with tears drying on his cheeks. I stood up noiselessly and tiptoed back into the house.

Dad's notice was stapled onto another document: a report from a geriatrician at the hospital, addressed to Marcia Ellis. I skimmed through four paragraphs describing the consultation: Dad's confident presentation and physical fitness set against his poor score on cognitive, language and memory tests; his failure to know the date or even the year. The consultant felt that concussion, thyroid dysfunction and various other conditions could be excluded as potential causes. He mentioned the results of a scan indicating the build-up of plaques in Dad's brain, and felt confident in diagnosing Alzheimer's disease. He commented that Dr Kirkland's active lifestyle and coping mechanisms may have masked the developing symptoms for some years. He gave advice about managing the condition, drugs that might slow its progression.

Marcia would have given Dad the news. I doubted it came as a surprise to him. He understood what it meant and where it would take him. He must have wanted to remind himself of the ghastly truth.

FELIX, YOU HAVE ALZHEIMER'S

I sat down in his armchair, paralysed by indecision, the papers trembling in my hand. My instinct was to get rid of them—otherwise he'd have to relive today's terror over and over again. Surely I should spare him that?

In the end, though, it wasn't my choice. I pinned everything back onto the noticeboard and left the room.

Truth mattered to my father.

EIGHTEEN

It was a sound to gladden the heart of every farmer in the district: thundering on the tin roof. Sustained, glorious April rain. I snuggled into my pillow, imagining water soaking into the thirsty landscape.

How many times had I listened to this drumming, lying in this same bed? Sometimes it brought me joy, because it meant the school cross-country would be cancelled. Oh, how I dreaded the cross-country. Whippet-fast kids like Leah and Ira would romp in well ahead of the pack. My siblings might come somewhere in the top ten. And all those smug bastards would be tucking into the sausage sizzle by the time I stumbled red-faced up to the finish line, humiliated by the patronising applause of other people's parents.

The downpour stopped at dawn. The sun blazed, steam rose from the paddocks and a vivid rainbow arched across the foothills. I took a photo for Nathan. He replied immediately: *Get out there and find that pot of gold!* The same afternoon the heavens opened again.

Nathan was right: there was a pot of gold. Rain and sunshine had a magical effect on both landscape and people. The air tasted sweet. Paddocks greened up overnight—you could almost hear the plants and trees growing. Taciturn farmers wore grins, locals greeted one another on Tawanui's main street with talk of the lovely rain.

'That's farming for you,' declared Ira, a week or so later. He was putting up electric tape in the paddock bordering our garden. 'We'll all be stressing about something else next month. Facial eczema, or too much grass.'

He seemed unusually chirpy today. He'd even had a haircut.

'Hey, Ira,' I said. 'Are you still seeing that . . . whoever it was you were dating?'

I caught the flash of a grin—swiftly suppressed, but not fast enough.

'I knew it!' I cried. 'Who is she? Anyone I know?'

He rolled his eyes, muttering about nosy friends. 'Nobody you know,' he said, when he realised I wasn't going to give up. 'She's from Dunedin. One of the vets.'

With very little prompting, he proceeded to tell me about her children: Alex and Sean, aged eight and six, who were 'neat little guys'. Alex was already a keen reader, Sean was mad on soccer. He also had Down's syndrome, but neither he nor his mother let that get in the way of anything.

I listened with a growing sense of wonder. Ira's life was changing. This woman, and her children, were taking up residence in his world.

'What's her name?' I asked.

'Cathy.'

'With a C or a K? Why'd she come up from Dunedin? Where does she live?'

Ira scowled. He wasn't fooling me, though; I knew him far too well. I could tell he was happy.

'With a C. Came up to be near the boys' grandparents, who live in Hastings. Their dad died in a cycling accident. For Pete's sake, don't breathe a word to Mum. She'll be planning the wedding.'

'Raewyn knows there's someone,' I told him. 'She is all-seeing, all-knowing.'

He laughed as he stooped to unhook a connection on the perimeter fence. Rain began to speckle the wooden rails and posts. I had a moment of nostalgia, remembering the pair of us prancing around on the woolshed roof with our mouths wide open and our heads back, catching raindrops. That was back in the days when I just *knew* that Ira and I would get married.

'Thinking about having that test,' he said, so tonelessly and casually that I didn't understand what he meant. My mind was on the rain. I assumed he meant some kind of soil test for the farm.

'Test?' I blinked stupidly, and then the penny dropped. 'Oh! To find out if you're carrying . . .?'

'Yep. That.' He began laying the tape, stepping backwards as he unrolled it from the spool. 'Not my idea of fun, to sit there and have a total stranger tell me whether I'm a walking time bomb or not. I'm not saying I'm definitely going to do it. Just thinking about it.'

'Is this because of Cathy?'

He kept on walking backwards.

'D'you remember,' he said, 'what mealtimes were like at our place, when my dad couldn't use a knife anymore? Mum had to cut things up for him, so he only needed a fork. But he held it funny.'

I nodded. I remembered Manu's clawed hand.

'He used to drop it,' said Ira. 'We'd take it in turns to pick it up for him. In the end, Mum started giving him finger food, but he'd drop that too. He'd miss his mouth, or he'd put it in and forget how to swallow. I used to sit with my eyes shut and my hands over my ears. I came round to your place for meals whenever I could. Your parents were kind to me and Leah. I'll always be grateful for that.'

He turned away, picking up a pile of plastic fence posts from his quad bike.

'I don't want any child sitting with his eyes shut so he doesn't have to see me missing my mouth. And Cathy has kids. So maybe I have to get tested.'

I had a deluge of questions. When might he take it, and what would he do if it was negative—or positive? And how did he feel about—

'Would you care to give me a hand,' he suggested, interrupting me, 'instead of the third degree?'

I dropped down from the stile and swished my way through the wet grass, poking posts into the ground at intervals along the tape.

'Gyp and Gloria need to go to the vet,' I said. 'Urgently.'

'That's a coincidence.'

'No, but they do! They're due for their jabs.'

'You'll be sadly disappointed. Cathy doesn't work with small animals if she can help it. Mind you, last week she did emergency surgery on a guinea pig.'

I stopped teasing him and got on with the job. We worked quite efficiently together, until the temporary fence was up and young Friesian bulls were tearing away at the new grass as though they'd not had a mouthful in weeks.

'Is our eel still living in the river?' I asked.

'Kikorangi.' He chuckled. 'Old girl left years ago. She must have set off on her last journey, home to Tonga or wherever. Hope she made it.'

'Perhaps her children have come back.'

'It's possible. There's a couple of eels living in her pool now. Might be her kids.'

Afterwards, he dropped into the house for coffee. He left his boots on the porch, sat at the table and had an in-depth conversation with Dad about water purity regulations for the Tukituki catchment.

If you closed one eye and squinted a bit, life looked almost normal.

Until it wasn't.

NINETEEN

The dogs and I were home from our morning expedition to the letterbox. Mum called while we were walking back, and was still on the line as I clumped up the porch steps. It's amazing how much we found to gossip about.

'Is Nathan still with that girl?' she asked.

'Yup.' I was shuffling through the post, the phone jammed under my chin. Nothing interesting.

'He sent me a postcard from a beautiful beach,' she said. 'Oh, to be young and in love again!'

Gloria and Gyp had bustled down to Dad's bedroom, leaving damp paw marks every step of the way. I heard his voice: 'Hello! You two been for a walk, hey? You're wet!' It was getting on for coffee time: that happy hour, both of us at our best. Once Mum had rung off, I put the kettle on before going in search of him.

I found him dressed in his usual collared shirt, jersey and canvas trousers, kneeling beside the neatly made bed, looking into his green steel trunk. It had belonged to his great-uncle Bert, a regular soldier who made it through both world wars, and had the letters *A.W.K.*—for Albert William Kirkland—stencilled above the latch.

'Morning, Dad. Sleep well?'

'I think so.' He was stacking three box files in a pile. They looked worn, their edges buckling. 'Now ... these are your boxes. I keep them in Bert's army chest, so they're always there to remind me.'

'*My* boxes?'

'You children. You, pl ... pl ... agh! My stupid brain! Plu ... ral. That's it.'

He pushed himself to his feet before stooping to pick up the top one. Blue capital letters marching across the lid: *EMILY*. I was baffled.

'This is yours,' he announced, looking pleased with himself.

'What's in it?'

'Um, well. Let's have a look. The only good thing about going peculiar, as I am, is that life is full of surprises.'

I followed him to the kitchen. One end of the table was clear, so he put the box down there.

'Let's see. What's in the box? What's in the box?' He looked at me, blinking. 'Those words sound awfully ominous. Is it a quote from somewhere?'

'*Seven.*'

'Seven?'

'A thriller,' I said. 'Brilliant film. There's a severed head in the box.'

'Oh gosh!' He made a comical, pretend-shocked face. 'How very gruesome. Well, anyway. What's in *this* box, with your name on the lid? Not a severed head, I hope.'

He lifted the lid. We both looked in.

Not a severed head.

It was full to the brim, mainly of paper and card and photographs of all colours and sizes. On the top lay something I didn't remember ever having seen before: a micro-sized handprint—*my* handprint, apparently!—about three inches long, in exuberant yellow poster paint, cut out and stuck onto blue card. Underneath, some teacher had written *Happy Father's Day from . . .* and beneath that was a collection of indecipherable scribblings— my preschool attempt to sign my name.

'Dad,' I breathed, putting my adult hand on top of that tiny print, 'what is all this?'

'Your memories. Did you really not know I had these?'

We sat at right angles to one another at the table. I picked things out of the box, smoothing them, reverentially laying them in rows. First out were nursery school paintings, splodges of primary colour. Skies were wiggly blue streaks along the top of the paper; faces were two eyes, a nose and a mouth in no particular order.

'I was hardly a child prodigy,' I said.

'Oh, I don't know.' Dad held one of them up to the light. 'These would cause a stir in the Tate Modern. Say you painted them last week.'

'I'll do that. I'll call them a faux-naive representation of the existential crisis of humanity today.'

He chuckled, while I pulled the next piece of toddler artwork from the file.

I'm sure parents all over the world keep boxes like these, full of precious garbage. In my studio in the flat I had two drawers dedicated to Nathan memorabilia. Yet I'd never seen this collection of Dad's before. I had no idea that he'd held on to a single souvenir from any of our childhoods, especially mine, since I was the dunce of the family in both academic and sporting terms. I was dumbfounded to discover that he'd not only collected a treasure trove of memories, but that he'd stashed it all in Uncle Bert's army trunk, right beside his bed.

Deeper into the box, my attempts at art became progressively less clumsy: more paintings, little clay sculptures, even a ragged piece of embroidery. Poems and essays. Programs from local productions, when I was the set designer, and—Dear Lord, what was this?—my first published work: a page from the school magazine with a copy of a stained-glass window I'd made out of cellophane. And look! Further down the pile, a sketch of an otter, in charcoal. I remembered copying it meticulously from a book in the school library, trying so hard to capture the water droplets on his fur and the expression in his eyes. I proudly brought it home, and Mum stuck it to a cupboard door in the kitchen, along with a whole load of other rubbish I'd produced. It hung there until it was peeling at the corners. I never gave a thought to what happened to it after that. Now I knew.

'Ah, yes. *Otter*,' said Dad, holding out his hand to take it from me. 'This was a marvellously accurate study. The water on his fur. Look, even the glint in his eye! I was most impressed.'

'But you never said so.'

'Oh, I expect I did. People never listen to a word I say.'

'No.' I held my ground. 'No, Dad. You didn't. Mum put it on the cupboard, but I don't think you mentioned it at all. I would have been chuffed.'

'Well, one can't go flattering children too much. It's not good for them. My mother never paid me a compliment, on principle. Nor Helen. I got into Oxford, the first in our family, but when I opened the letter—you can imagine my excitement! This was my dream!—she only said, "Don't become big-headed."'

Nana Kirkland's repressive attitude had obviously rubbed off. All through my school life, I heard other parents bragging about their kids. *She's in the Orienteering Nationals, they say she's a natural.* Or, *She's got an amazing singing voice! Can't think where she gets it from.* Or even simply, *He's a good lad. Never lets me down.* But I never heard Dad express pride in any of us, not even Carmen, who worked fiendishly hard—she had to, frankly; she's not half as bright as she pretends to be—and whose exam grades were *almost* as good as Leah's.

The final straw was my university graduation. My friends' parents turned up in droves, all misty-eyed, took reels of photos and whooped loudly as their offspring crossed the stage. I was insufferable when Nathan graduated—in floods of happy tears, and I'd have plastered gushing posts all over Facebook if he hadn't categorically forbidden it.

But my family? Nope. No cheerleaders. Mum was back in England by then. My siblings weren't interested. I asked Dad, and to my surprise and delight he said of course he'd come! So I booked a seat for him. I had everything planned weeks in advance, was so looking forward to it. He was going to drive up to Auckland on the day, stay in a hotel and take me out to dinner.

But he cancelled on the morning of the ceremony. One of his patients had an emergency, a premature baby—and she, of course, must come first. I harboured the bitter suspicion that he didn't think a BA in Fine Arts was worth his valuable time. That was the day I swore I would never rely on my family for affirmation ever again. *Sod 'em. Sod the effing bastards*, I was thinking as I marched defiantly across the stage in a hired gown, mortarboard and ragged espadrilles. *Sod the effing lot of 'em. I don't need them.*

'Oh, look!' breathed Dad, reaching into the far corner of the box. 'Look at this!'

He was holding out a tiny plastic bracelet: *Kirkland, Emily Alice, 7 lb 2 oz.* I took the flimsy object from his hand, running it between my fingers, pressing it briefly to my cheek. He'd kept it. All these years he'd cherished this piece of plastic, just because I had worn it for the first hours of my life. He'd brought it all the way to New Zealand. Had he taken it out of this box sometimes, and looked at it?

'You were so sweet! A very even-tempered baby.' Laughter began in the corner of his eyes, a crinkling of mischief. 'Hard to imagine now!'

And then he was overcome with wheezy chuckles, clutching his head.

'Dad!' I protested, though I was laughing with him.

He took the bracelet back from me, smiling fondly. 'Kirkland, Emily Alice . . . You are just exactly right, in every way.'

I think this was the greatest compliment he had ever paid me.

He was rootling in the box again.

'I like this one of you,' he said, dragging a photo out of a plastic pocket.

My graduation portrait. The official photographer waited like a troll under a bridge, leaping out to grab unsuspecting graduates as they escaped from the stage—*Stop here!*—lined her victims up against a wall one by one, ordered them to smile and blinded them with her flash. Even in my furious misery, I bowed to convention when a giant camera lens was pointed in my direction—holding up my new certificate, forcing a deranged grin. A vast spot glowed on my chin, and the mortarboard slipped to a clownish angle. *Flash*.

'How come you've got this?' I asked, as he gave it to me. 'You must have ordered it.'

'Must have.'

'But you weren't even at my graduation.'

He looked puzzled. 'Wasn't I?'

'No, you bloody well weren't! You had an emergency at work, a premature baby or something. You cancelled on the day—on the *day*, Dad.'

I intended to sound light-hearted, but it came out in a yell. I'd been nursing my precious pet of resentment for over a quarter of a century. Sometimes I could actually taste it—a sourness at the back of my throat.

'I'm sure I . . .' He stopped, blinked, wrinkled his forehead. 'Now, now. Was I, though? I do have some memory of that occasion. No, you're right. Your mother was absolutely livid. She phoned me up from England just to shout at me.'

'*I* was livid, Dad.'

'I think'—he rapped his knuckles on the table—'I think it was when that poor young woman made a determined effort to drown herself . . . oh, what was her name? The family were farming way, way up under the mountains. New baby, postpartum psychosis. The husband woke up in the morning, heard the baby crying but there was no sign of the mother. Found her face down in a dam. She was lucky to survive.'

'That's terrible.'

'Mm, it *was* terrible. We had to wait for the psychiatric team to arrive, you see. Waited for hours. She was psychotic; I couldn't just bundle her into an ambulance. There were several small children, and the husband had fallen apart, he sat and cried . . . I had to stay with them. But the timing was disastrous, because of your graduation. I was so sorry. I've always felt very bad about that.'

I looked again at the photo: a plump girl with waves of brown hair, blue eyes, a spot on her chin and a fake smile. I felt sorry for her.

'Why didn't you tell me the whole story at the time?' I asked. He looked surprised at the question.

'It was a matter of confidentiality. I was in their house when I phoned you, using their telephone! I had to be very careful. You're a doctor's daughter—you understand these things, surely?'

'I forgive you,' I said, smiling—and it dawned on me that I really *had* forgiven him. That sour taste was gone.

'I love your otter,' he said, holding it up. 'Have you seen this? Very clever.'

'Ah, the otter.' I was getting slicker at pretending we hadn't had these conversations already. 'Yes, I was proud of that one.'

'Look at the glint in this creature's eye. Look at his wet fur.'

We sat close together and sifted through that crumpled hoard of memories, chatting, exclaiming quietly over treasures. Another shower of rain came through, followed by watery sun. Dad recalled events from decades ago: the books I read, the friends I brought home, the names of pets. He seemed enchanted to be reminiscing with me. I felt a calm kind of lightness, a euphoria.

'Dad,' I said, 'I wish you'd told me you were saving all these things. I wish I'd known.'

'It's no secret. Everyone knows I can't throw anything away.'

'Yes, but this isn't just not throwing them away, is it? You took the otter down from the kitchen cupboard. You saved my baby bracelet. You ordered my graduation photo.'

He laid his forearm flat on the table, stretching his fingers towards mine, though he didn't quite touch them.

'Of course! These were memories of you. We always used to chat, didn't we? You and I? Even when you were small, we talked about all kinds of things. We walked up to Biddulph's, remember that day? By Jove, you gave that all you'd got. It was a highlight for me.'

'I thought I was a nuisance, spoiling your hike.'

'I was thrilled! But so cross with myself for not choosing an easier walk for our first outing. And one time we lay on the trampoline, talking about the stars.'

As time passed, he gradually fell silent. His hands began to tremble and lose their grip. The mist was seeping in again. Near the bottom of the box I found a picture of myself in a hospital gown, looking red-faced and happy, cuddling newborn Nathan. Hoping to bring Dad back, I showed it to him.

'Isn't this the most beautiful baby you ever saw?' I gushed.

He peered at the picture. 'She looks like a nice young lady.'

'That's me.'

He laughed awkwardly, murmuring that he didn't think so. He seemed to think I was joking, and I felt a stab of hurt. Irrational, I know.

'C'mon, Dad.' I drew a circle in the air around my own face. 'Me. I'm holding Nathan.'

He stared from the photo to my face, and back again. 'But where is this baby now? And where is this very young woman? Is it Helen?'

'No, it's me.'

'My sister Helen had a baby, but she died.'

'I know.'

'They sent me a bloody telegram! *Helen died today after giving birth to a stillborn son.* I've still got it. I stood at the porter's lodge and read those words, and . . . it was . . . oh!' He made a chopping gesture with his right hand.

'I'm sorry, Dad.'

'I should've stayed at home. I should never have left her with them.'

He was on his feet, barging outside and down the porch steps. Gyp and Gloria followed close behind like two tail-waving bodyguards. I wondered what those faithful dogs made of their master's erratic moods.

Our blissful hour was over. Just another memory. Sighing, I stowed everything back in the box: the graduation photo, the otter, the handprint, the baby bracelet, all those other scraps. I could have cried for the lost years when I'd deliberately avoided my father. It was almost too late now. The shadows of his life were lengthening.

•

Raewyn joined us for an early dinner. I left the *EMILY* box out, thinking Dad might like to show her. It worked its magic. The pair of them took a companionable trip down memory lane—*See the otter? Look at the water on his fur!*—while I did the washing-up and answered emails.

Nathan sent a happy selfie of himself and Ella, both holding up bowls of noodles and grinning. There was a market in the background, throngs of people, coloured lights. They were on their way to Flores, where they hoped to see Komodo dragons.

Did I know, he asked, that the Komodo dragon is the largest creature on this planet to be able to reproduce without a male?

Crikey! I replied. *That's a superpower worth having.*

By now the sun was sliding behind the ranges, flooding the sky with a last half-hour of glory. At Raewyn's suggestion, she and Dad nipped out for a stroll.

Once they'd gone, I took the box back to Dad's room. The two others were still on the floor beside Bert's trunk: *EDWARD* and *CARMEN*. A brief look inside them both revealed more or less what I expected: school reports, science fair projects, merit certificates. Carmen's wedding invitation:

> *The marriage of Carmen and Richard*
> *Saturday, 11th June 1994*

I leafed through a small album of her wedding photos. There we all were, among the bare winter vines, with the Ruahines as our backdrop: blue sky, sunlit snow on the peaks. Carmen was a stylish bride, I had to admit, poured into an art deco gown. Crimson lipstick. No bust, of course, while I had rather too much. She'd gone flaxen blonde, and Mum had given her ringlets with the electric rollers. Richard, with his slightly gormless good looks, was her dapper fashion accessory.

There were pictures of Mum in a peach suit, smiling, a glass in her hand; Eddie with his delicate chin jutting. I was one of the trio of bridesmaids in floaty dresses.

And Dad: neat features, vivid blue eyes with their network of creases. He still had plenty of hair, though with a distinguished tint of pewter, and that upright posture. Yet he seemed oddly detached from the scene. In fact, for the father of the bride, he looked pretty miserable.

I stacked our three boxes back in Bert's chest. I was about to close the lid when I spotted a fourth. Forest green, dog-eared, innocuous.

HER
REMEMBER!

How intriguing. This one must be souvenirs of Mum. *HER*. The One. He loved her after all! Every child likes to kid themselves that their parents adore one another, even when those parents are long divorced; even when that child is middle-aged and has an adult son of her own, and has never really been in love herself.

Discarding the lid, I snatched up the first thing that came to hand: a square photo. I honestly expected to see a picture of my mother, young and happy.

There was a young woman in the photo, but it wasn't Mum. *Leah*.

Leah in shorts and a strappy singlet, draped like a mermaid on a moss-covered rock, her feet in the rushing current of a stream. A hint of bright sky, the spider's web of a tree fern. Sunlight glinted on the water, on her tanned shoulders, on the muscular contours of her legs.

Well, okay. Many hikers would be lightly dressed in summer. And yet . . . both shoulder straps had slipped down her arms, and she was quite clearly wearing nothing underneath. There was something unmistakably playful about her body language: hands resting on the rock behind her, the way she was pouting in a mocking imitation of a supermodel. The serious academic seemed to be blowing a kiss at the camera. And that singlet was dripping wet, clinging to her curves. The effect was undeniably sensual.

Dear God, I thought. *She was sleeping with whoever took this photo. What's it doing in a box beside my father's bed?*

Voices, right outside my window. Dad and Raewyn were in the garden, chatting about compost and aphids while I held a picture of Leah in my hand. I ought to stop, right now. I ought to shut everything back in Bert's chest, walk out of the room and forget the existence of a box marked *HER*. These were Dad's memories, his life. I had no right to invade his privacy.

Yet I was desperate for an innocent explanation. There *had* to be one. Perhaps someone else in the tramping club took this photo? They might all have gone up in a big group. This happened about once a year, when the club called for volunteers to fix trails or huts.

Under the photo lay a jumbled pile of papers. Some were folded, some torn. The first seemed to be the torn-off flap of an envelope. Someone had scribbled across it—sharp, angular handwriting, each letter leaning forwards as though straining to get to the end of the line.

I shouldn't have read it. But I did.

I'm back. Tomorrow, usual time and place.
Will wait, but can't wait.
L

I could actually feel the smashing of my heart against my chest. Hyper-alert for sounds of Dad and Raewyn, I scrabbled through the box. My fingers were clumsy. I felt physically sick, but I couldn't look away.

All the notes were covered with that confident hand, all faded and mildewed. They probably dated back to the very last days before mobile phones and the internet transformed the way people carry on affairs. Landlines might so easily be answered by the wrong person: a wife, colleague, flatmate, child. These correspondents were careful, whoever they were. No names, no identifying details beyond the initial, L. Perhaps they used a post office box, or had a secret drop-off place?

The next two I read were on blue writing paper, which in itself seemed dated. From the look of the creases, the sheets had been folded in half, and in half again.

My love,

I've been thinking about you too. I never stop thinking about you. I never will. I never believed this was possible.

I can't come on Weds. I'm so sorry. The meeting I mentioned is going ahead.

But never mind—we have all of next week!

L

My love,

I found your message. It didn't surprise me. I knew you'd be in agony about our decision. Yes, it's breaking the rules. Yes, people will talk. And yes, of course I want to go on.

These past few days were not wrong, and you know it. They were inevitable. They were the beginning of our future.

I love you. We love one another. Have you any idea of the rarity of that?

We'll have all of our lives together. How wonderful.

I'll be back on the 5th.

L

The fourth was scribbled on a ruled page.

NO! I do not, I will not regret what we are doing. This is not routine, not something to be discarded.

I won't allow the petty rules of society to get in the way! You and I, we

Footsteps on the porch had me scrambling. I stuffed that last note in my pocket, everything else back into the box, and was closing the lid on Bert's chest when Raewyn called from the kitchen.

'I'm just off, Emily. Thanks for dinner.'

I'm sure I was gabbling like a goose as I rushed along to say goodbye. I had a weird sense of disconnect. *Leah Leah Leah.*

'Are you okay to walk back?' I asked. 'Shall I drive you? Want to borrow a torch?'

No, she said, smiling. She didn't need a torch. She'd go home by the road, there was plenty of light.

Dad and I stood on the porch and watched the indomitable figure marching away. I was relieved when he said he was tired and took himself off to read in his bedroom. After glimpsing some of the contents of the green box, I couldn't look him in the eye.

Later, in the sanctuary of my own room, I pulled that stolen note from my pocket and smoothed it flat.

NO! I do not, I will not regret what we are doing. This is not routine, not something to be discarded.

I won't allow the petty rules of society to get in the way! You and I, we are not ordinary. What we are together is not ordinary. Hang your conscience. What has any of this to do with morality? Who are we harming?

I don't bestow love on just anybody.

L

I stood up, sat down, stood up. Kicked the cupboard and stubbed my toe. She was the same age as his own children! He was a married—maybe divorced—community doctor. Her family were his patients. She looked like an adult in that photo by the stream, but how old was she when this began?

For most of my life, I'd felt weighed down by my failure to live up to my father's standards. He couldn't possibly turn out to be a philandering, two-timing cradle-snatcher who abused his profession. He was a good doctor and dutiful husband whose Wife Didn't Understand Him.

Bloody hell, bloody hell. Did she seduce him—or the other way around—when he was oh-so-solicitously delivering palliative care to poor Manu? Perhaps they shagged in my parents' bedroom while Mum was at work in the library! Only a few hours earlier I'd been so happy, so touched, to find my graduation photograph among his hoard; now I wondered whether he was cavorting with Leah while it was taken. At the very moment I was plastering on a grin for the official photographer, she might have been pouting in her wet singlet.

I leaned my forehead against the window. Bands of cerulean and acid green gleamed behind the saddle above Biddulph's bivvy. Memories were being violently shaken, rising to the surface. Dad was the first to go up there—up *there*, to that rugged silhouette beneath the gleaming green sky—to look for her. He led teams day after day, searching, searching, barely even stopping to eat. He cared. He cared *so much*. Why did he care so much?

My phone flashed, the blare of sound startling me. I was about to switch it off when I saw that my caller was Sarah.

She was in a good mood.

'Hello!' she cried. 'How's the back of beyond?'

'Okay.'

'Freezing here, so much for spring. Look, I just wanted to let you know that I love what you've done with the Queen's fluffy mule slippers. You're a genius.'

I sat down on my bed, massaging the side of my neck with one hand.

'You all right?' she asked.

'Not really.'

I described what I'd found in the box. I read the note to her.

'So, let me get this straight,' she said. 'The girl's not stark bollock naked in this pic?'

'She's wearing shorts and a singlet.'

'Hardly pornographic, is it? Just someone cooling off on a hot day, during a trek. Wearing trekking clothes.'

'I think whoever took that picture was Leah's lover. I can tell. It's the sort of photo you wouldn't show your mum, if you know what I mean. And there's no mistaking the notes. They're not steamy, they're mawkish and kind of old-fashioned, but they are definitely love letters. They've been kept in a box by his bed, with *HER* written on the lid, in what looks like his handwriting. And they're signed "L". I can't think of an innocent explanation.'

I could hear Toby in the background, nagging his mother to give him the phone so he could talk to me. He and I were mates.

'Shush for a minute, you menace,' whispered Sarah.

I heard her bribing him with a chocolate biscuit, promising he could talk to me when the little hand on the clock was pointing straight up. Then she was back on the line.

'Okay, Emily. Let's think laterally.'

Bless my friend. She obviously thought I was overreacting, but she did her best to calm me down, to be a voice of reason.

'Doing a back-of-an-envelope calculation,' she began, 'I'd estimate approximately half a billion people on the planet have a name that begins with "L". Your mother's Lillian, isn't she? Maybe she found herself some extracurricular activity. Maybe *she* wrote those letters, but not to your dad.'

I pictured Mum: bitter, lonely, homesick.

'Not her handwriting,' I said. 'And not her in the photo.'

'Okay then, here's an even simpler explanation: what if Leah was having a fling with your brother?'

I couldn't imagine any sane woman—perhaps apart from his wife, Rhonda—declaring her love for Eddie, least of all Leah. Still, there was no doubting the fact that he was obsessed with her for years, and they did have that tiff at Carmen's wedding.

'But why the big secret?' I asked. 'They were both adults, both single. Childhood friends. There was no need for all this cloak-and-dagger stuff. And why would Dad have all their notes in a box by his bed?'

'Secret . . . secret. Could your sister have been involved with Leah? What's her name again?'

'Carmen.'

'Carmen and Leah.' Sarah sounded delighted with this new theory. 'Ticks all the boxes. I imagine a gay fling would've set off some pearl-clutching in your home town all those decades ago?'

Thinking of Todd Tillerson, I agreed that it might.

'But I don't think this involves Carmen,' I said. 'She and Richard are about to celebrate their silver wedding.'

'So what? She could be bi. The most conventional folk are often repressing something. Remind me what that note said?'

'*I won't allow the petty rules of society to get in the way*,' I read. '*You and I, we are not ordinary. What we are together is not ordinary.*'

'The rules of society,' repeated Sarah. 'Carmen and Leah, the love that dare not speak its name. Perhaps your dad discovered this collection of letters after you'd all left home, and decided they shouldn't be thrown out. He might have intended to give them back to Carmen someday.'

I was dredging up memories of my sister. The horses, the hysteria at exam time, the school dances. She went to all those snog-fests, dressed up to the nines, always with one of a succession of young men. But then she *would* go with boys, wouldn't she? Todd Tillerson pretended to Leah's boyfriend just to fit in with everybody's expectations. Perhaps Leah dated him for precisely the same reason.

But Carmen didn't just dance with those guys. I knew this for a fact. I used to find it hilarious to barge into her bedroom and catch her making out with the latest gangling yoof—*Bloody hell, Emily, don't you ever knock?* I never saw anything like that when it came to her female friends.

'It's an ingenious theory,' I said in the end, 'but no. I'm not buying it.'

Toby was back. The little hand on the clock was pointing straight up, and he wasn't going to be fobbed off again. 'My turn to talk! I've got to tell Emily about the puddle!'

'Put him on,' I said. 'My favourite little guy.'

It was cheering to hear my godson's baby voice, to glimpse his worldview. He regaled me with a very long, *very* complicated story about a puddle he jumped into, and I giggled with him about getting so wet—*even my pants were wet!* Then he declared that he could count to thirty now, and would I like to hear him?

'Off you go then,' I said, so off he went. He had a rock-solid grasp of numbers as far as ten, after which he chirpily made them up, *eleventeen, fifty-ninety*, until Sarah took the phone back off him.

'Look, Emily, why not ask your father straight out? Tell him you've found all this stuff. He might be able to explain everything.'

'I can't do that!'

'You're not going to rest until you have. Our parents are human beings too. They make monumental cock-ups, just like us. If it turns out that he and Leah were together for a while, all those years ago . . . well, would it really matter?'

'Thirteee!' crowed Toby.

●

The world seemed horribly lonely after we said goodbye. I fell back onto the pillow and lay with my eyes shut.

Why did it matter if Dad and Leah once had an affair? It mattered because it made him a different person. It mattered because Leah had disappeared. It mattered because there was a very distinctive beanie in Carmen's cupboard.

And if it was Leah's, then I was not the last person to see her alive.

TWENTY

I spent the next morning trying to behave naturally towards Dad, despite what I'd found in that box.

To add to all the fun, Eddie and Carmen had held bilateral discussions and announced a state visit to Arapito in a fortnight's time. Eddie was booked to run workshops in Napier and Palmerston North, so Tawanui wasn't too much of a detour; Carmen would take a couple of days off work, cadge a lift with him and stay with various friends. They planned to stop for lunch with us on their way through.

Hope this date is okay with you, Eddie had written, as though I had a choice.

'What an honour,' I said to Dad. 'Usually I have to go on a tour of the country for an audience with either of 'em.'

'You don't sound very . . .'

'Enthusiastic? Well, it's nice of them to include us on their road trip, but I think they've got an agenda.'

'Ah.' He smiled vaguely as he opened the biscuit tin. 'Nothing worse than one of those.'

I'd woken up to a message from Sarah: *Have you asked your Dad about that girl yet? Communication is the key!*

'Dad,' I began, 'I wondered . . .'

'Biscuit?'

He stood with the tin in his hand, offering me one of Raewyn's delights. He rarely ate them himself anymore. He complained that nothing tasted right. He was losing weight, his clothes hanging off him.

I couldn't do it. I couldn't ask something so deeply personal. I chose a biscuit, mumbled something about needing to crack on with work and scurried off.

I was telling the truth about work. I lack self-discipline. I don't run marathons or maintain long-term relationships and I've never managed to put my holiday snaps in an album, but in my line of work the secret to being in constant employment is to be reliable. Give me a deadline and I will meet it. In this case it meant producing a full set of mixed-media paintings, plus line drawings and smaller sketches, by mid-July. By hook or by crook, I was going to bring the Admiral and his friends to life again.

In the late afternoon I glanced outside to see Dad wandering among his roses. He bowed his head to look at something on one of the leaves. A pair of fantails swooped and flitted—up, down, around—almost landing on him, as though they were showing off to a favourite grandfather.

Even wild birds trusted my dad. A good doctor, of impeccable character, gently pottering in his garden.

A good doctor.

Of impeccable character.

I had to ask him.

I slipped into his room to grab the photo from Bert's chest. Sarah was right: I should be upfront. He'd have an explanation, and that would be an end of it. By the time I joined him outside, he'd fetched his secateurs from the toolshed and was deadheading roses with the precision of a surgeon. Snap, snap.

'Hello there!' He glanced up at me with a placid smile, laying the secateurs down on a wheelbarrow. 'Aren't these looking good?'

I approached, holding out the photograph in both hands. I was having second thoughts now, but it was too late. He'd spotted it.

'What have you got there?' he asked.

'I found . . . I just wondered . . . is this your photo?'

As I handed over my burden, he felt in the top pocket of his shirt for his reading glasses. He put them on. He stood motionless, head bent, holding the picture a few inches from his face. And then, to my horror, tears began inching their way down the furrows beside his nose.

'I'm sorry,' he whimpered. 'Sorry, sorry.'

Gently at first, he began to rock from side to side, crooning. It was a horribly disturbing sound, like a very drunk person trying to sing to a child. My father, who only yesterday had failed to recognise a photograph of me and my baby son, was falling to pieces over this relic of Leah Parata.

He crumpled the picture in his fist, forcing it into his shirt pocket. Fumbling, sobbing, he snatched up the secateurs and beheaded a glorious sunrise-coloured rose, the most perfect bloom on his precious border, one of his few remaining pleasures. The stricken flower tumbled down among the stems, scattering soft petals.

'Hey!' I cried, rushing to pick it up. 'This is a lovely one. Let me save it, I'll put it in water.'

He ignored me. He chose another perfect flower, and another, destroying each with livid precision.

'Happy?' he asked, without looking at me. 'Happy now? Are you happy now?'

'Dad, please stop!'

'They're diseased. Look at the leaves.'

Only a few perfect little buds were left, but even these innocents weren't spared. He savaged them, shaking the branches until they'd fallen all the way to the ground. Once every bush was shorn of colour he performed a shuffling, stomping dance on the beds, crushing the delicate petals with his feet, grinding them into the soil. Such destruction. Such rage.

Meanwhile I too danced around, begging him to stop. Unwisely, I tried to take the secateurs away from him. He reacted fast—swinging them up and jabbing the blades towards my face as I backed away.

'Bugger off!' He was glaring at me with seething hatred. 'Who are you, to come into my garden? What are you doing here? Get out!'

This wasn't him. This wasn't my dad. It was the opposite of him, the Hyde to his Jekyll. I turned tail and sprinted back up the steps and into the house, ramming the sliding door shut with shaking hands. When I next looked out he was leaning against the fence, hair fluttering in the wind.

A cold weight of grief lodged in my stomach. It seemed as though I'd finally lost him. I was right off the map now. Should I call a doctor? An ambulance? Should I ask Raewyn to come over?

Not Raewyn. Never Raewyn. He had a photo of Leah in his pocket.

In the end I came down to practicalities, since that was all I could do. Dinner, I thought. He liked spaghetti bolognaise, so I'd try to tempt him with that. He'd hardly eaten a thing all day. Blood sugar.

My legs felt weak, my shaking hands were clumsy. I turned on the radio, seeking the companionship of human voices. It didn't help much.

The sun was low when he came in, removing his muddy shoes at the door and commenting on the loveliness of the evening.

'Been gardening?' I asked.

'Yes! Pruning the roses.'

He set off to his room, no doubt to change out of his gardening clothes. The crumpled photo was still in the breast pocket of
his shirt.

•

A plover woke me, or perhaps two or three of them, screeching
from the river.

After supper, while Dad was asleep in front of the news, I'd
crept into his room and peeked into Bert's chest, wondering
whether he'd replaced Leah's photo in the green box.

The boxes marked EMILY, CARMEN and EDWARD were
exactly as I'd stacked them earlier. The green one—HER—had
vanished.

The plover screeched again. The darkness was full of half-
glimpsed fears, jamming the airwaves in my mind. Decapitated
roses, secateurs, a turquoise beanie, a box full of secrets. I switched
on the lamp, shivering as I knelt on the floor to drag out my
suitcase. The envelope lay under my passport and spare jersey. It
looked innocent, but it felt malevolent. I'd assumed it only contained
his will, which might set off firecrackers in my siblings' heads, but
that was all. Nothing dangerous. Nothing life-destroying.

Truth matters, he'd said, as he handed it into my safekeeping.
History matters. And: *The contents could do a great deal of harm.*

I could open it right now, read whatever was inside, seal it up
again. Nobody need ever know.

But I didn't. Instead, I pushed it into the gap beneath the inner
lining of my suitcase, and slid everything back under my bed.
I even locked the case, as though I could somehow stop the truth
from spilling out.

Because if I looked inside, *I* would know. And I was becoming
very, very afraid of the truth.

TWENTY-ONE

The year was turning. Subtly, inexorably. The days grew shorter, the shadows longer, the sunlight thin and mellow as it gleamed through early-morning mists. Raewyn's apple and pear trees were laden with fruit, which she brought to us by the box load. We began to light the stove in the snug.

Dad's life was turning, too. Sometimes he still seemed much like the old Felix Kirkland, but often he wandered around on some unhappy mission of his own, his expression one of blank confusion. Digging in the garden seemed to be one of the few things that brought him any kind of contentment. I used to watch him moving piles of earth from one place to another before plodding into the kitchen, telling me what a productive afternoon it had been. The flowerbeds were covered in holes and piles of soil, as though a family of giant moles had taken up residence.

We had a visit from Dr Ellis, and another from Pamela, the practice nurse. I told them about his not being able to taste anything, about his weight loss, his increasing confusion. Pamela had some practical advice about providing lots of small snacks, but really all they could offer was sympathy. They both suggested getting in some home care, but I turned it down. *We can manage*, I said. *He guards his dignity.*

He and I still played chess most mornings. It was often warm enough to sit out on the porch, though we wore jerseys, sometimes hats and scarves. The day came when I won for the first time. I cheered and did a victory dance with my hands, assuming it must be a fluke. But it happened again, and again, until it was tricky not to win—and that was horrible. I took to sacrificing all my pieces, deliberately leaving them in the line of fire. I walked my king behind enemy lines, suicidally manoeuvring him into checkmate. It dawned on me that Dad was becoming confused about what the different pieces did, so I had to find ways to prompt him. Eventually, even these strategies stopped working. Our games became more and more bizarre, until they really weren't chess at all.

One terrible morning, he no longer knew how to set up the board. I emerged onto the porch with our coffee to find him anxiously fingering the pieces in their box, with others randomly scattered across the black and white squares. This man had been playing chess for about seventy years; whole lines of programming were being erased from his brain. The cruelty of that.

'Sorry,' he murmured. 'Not quite ready.'

He frowned up at me as he spoke, and I saw a lost child. I wanted to kneel down on the floor and hug him. Instead, I breezily set up the game, chattering, pretending I hadn't noticed a thing.

I blamed myself. I did. Somehow, I'd let go of his hand, and he was falling into the abyss. I was pretty sure I could hear his screams.

Soon he was insisting that we begin with a blank board and add pieces one by one in turn, as though we were playing noughts and crosses. We each took our turns very earnestly, but our games consisted entirely of made-up moves, like Toby counting to thirty.

It wasn't just chess that became a charade. Sudoku involved writing any old numbers in the spaces; crosswords were simply random letters. We would fill them in with gibberish, and then we'd congratulate ourselves on a job well done. And it was terrifying.

Increasingly often he slipped far away, into the mist. We'd sit in silence, both of us staring at the never-ending dance of light and shadow on the Ruahines.

One day, I asked him a dreaded question.

'Are you thinking about Leah, Dad, when you look up there?'

'Who?'

'Leah.'

He seemed mystified, and I felt a rush of guilty relief.

After that, I too tried to forget about Leah. Even if she and Dad were once lovers, it was all irrelevant now. There was too much damage to be done. Their secret belonged in the long-gone past, and there it must remain.

•

'Where do people go?' I whispered to Raewyn and Ira when they dropped in with firewood. 'Where is his soul?'

Ira looked gloomy.

'I used to ask that. Same question. Where did my old man go? He left the building years before his heart stopped beating.'

Raewyn curled her fingers around her mug and said I seemed tired. That was an understatement. I hadn't felt so poleaxed since Nathan was a baby. Dad was up and wandering most nights nowadays, crying, trying to wash his shirts in the dishwasher, getting dressed 'for work'. He was napping in the study right now. I didn't have that luxury.

'I'm okay,' I said, biting back a yawn. 'Dreading tomorrow, though. Carmen and Eddie are parachuting in like the bloody SAS.'

'Are they?' growled Ira. 'Glad you warned me. I'll stay well clear.'

He drained his coffee cup, stretched his spine and said he'd unload the firewood. I jumped up, making *let-me-help* noises, but he waved me back to my seat.

'It'll only take five minutes. Get Mum to tell you about her batshit crazy plan. And please, talk her out of it.'

Raewyn and I watched as he clomped down the steps to his trailer and lowered the tailgate with a clang. His two working dogs leaped out and began a game with Gloria and Gyp, the four of them dashing around the garden.

'Batshit crazy plan?' I asked Raewyn.

'Oh. Well.' She ducked her head, as though she'd just said something silly. 'I don't know. I'm in two minds. It might not be the right thing to do at all.'

'Let's hear it.'

'The seventeenth of June will mark twenty-five years since the day we last saw Leah. She'd be fifty-one now. What might she have done with her life?'

'She'd already achieved more than most people ever do.'

Raewyn cast an anxious glance out at Ira, who was chucking logs around.

'A journalist from *The Courier* got in touch. They're planning to make something of the anniversary. They want to interview us, people involved in the search, the police.'

I whistled under my breath. No wonder Ira was hurling logs onto the pile with such ferocity.

'And this morning I had another call,' added Raewyn. 'Television news people, wanting to do a bit of a documentary!'

'What did you tell them?'

'I asked for time to decide. The anniversary's still six weeks away, but . . .' She pressed her hands flat down on the table. Her knuckles looked swollen today. 'I'm going to say yes. Ira thinks I'm out of my mind. Do *you* think I'm out of my mind, Emily?' She forced a gentle, self-deprecating chuckle. 'Don't answer that question! I just . . . I *must* do it. For Leah. It might jog somebody's memory. Perhaps someone gave her a lift. Those men saw a person walking along Biddulph Road in the early morning, wearing a hat like hers. That could have been Leah! Maybe she banged her head, got amnesia and walked out, was picked up by a tourist, and they fell in love, and went off together to live in some faraway part of the world. She might be in Israel, or Norway or, or . . . I mean, miracles do happen.'

'They do.'

She gave a heartbreaking little grimace. 'I know it's not likely, but it's possible. We just might get some news of her. If there's even the tiniest chance of finding her alive, we have to try.'

I said of course, anything was possible, but I was lying. Leah's photograph was plastered all over the national news for weeks after her disappearance. Even if people really do get amnesia from a bump on the head, someone would have recognised her. She wasn't carrying her passport. It was impossible for her to have left the country with no trace, unless through a sophisticated smuggling operation.

'She could have been working for the government,' said Raewyn. 'That's something I've wondered. Maybe she had to change her identity. She's got a life in New York right now, with a new name. But she would have found some way to tell us, wouldn't she?'

Knowledge isn't always power. Knowledge can make you feel like the worst, most cruel person in the world. As Raewyn poured out her false hopes, all I could see was my dad pressing that photo of Leah to his heart. All I could think about were those letters. Raewyn would know for sure whether the sloping handwriting was Leah's.

'Did she have a, um, a . . . I mean, d'you think she *was* seeing anyone?' I asked.

'If she was, she never told me. I had the sense not to pry. She was an adult, she had her own life in Wellington. She was focused on protecting the planet. That was her greatest love.'

I love you. We love one another. Have you any idea of the rarity of that?

'There were all kinds of silly rumours,' Raewyn added. 'You'll have heard them too, I'm sure. About her having a boyfriend who hit her, made her frightened for her life. I heard one about her being pregnant—did you?'

'I did.'

'It was all rubbish. She spent a night at home before her trek, and she was coming back for another night afterwards. She turned up in the afternoon, in time to help me plant some fruit trees. We had a lovely time, gossiping about all kinds of things— Carmen's wedding, your travels, a girl she hoped Ira might fall for. We were reminiscing about what lovely childhoods they had despite poor Manu . . . There was no hint of her being pregnant, or anything like that. I nagged her about eating properly and she admitted she'd been living on toast and peanut butter, because she didn't have time to cook at the moment. She'd just marked three hundred exam papers! *I need a holiday now, Mum!* She was happy because she'd got confirmation that her team had the funding she needed. That was a big relief. She said how glad she was to be home.'

Raewyn laid her cheek in one hand, shaking her head. We listened to the clunk of logs being lobbed into place.

'I made pumpkin soup for her,' she said.

I didn't know what she meant. Stupid of me.

'On the Monday. Pumpkin soup and soda bread. The weather was so horrible, and I thought, *Oh dear, she'll be soaked through, this will warm her up!*' Raewyn was reciting a tale she knew by heart. 'She loved pumpkin soup. She always used to be ravenous when she got back from a hike, so I had everything ready on the table for her. I got the fire roaring, made sure we had lots of hot water for a shower. But . . .' A hopeless shrug. 'She never arrived. I kept listening for her car. Ira came in from the farm. He said,

Don't worry, Mum. Leah knows what she's doing, she'll have needed more time to survey all that massive area. She'll probably spend tonight in Biddulph's and walk out first thing tomorrow. So we waited until the next day, but she still didn't come home and . . . you start to think, *When do I call for help? When is this serious?* You start to imagine things. You imagine her lost. Hurt. Then suddenly it hits you that, no, this isn't right, it's been too long. You start making calls. That's when it becomes real. D'you remember, I phoned your dad?'

'I remember.'

'Hordes turned out to help. Todd Tillerson risked his job to drive up from Wellington and join in the search.'

'Todd did? I'd forgotten that.'

'Nice man.'

The four dogs bowed their heads to one another, mock-snarling while their tails waved. Ira stomped up and down the steps.

'My girl,' Raewyn said. 'I knew she might be suffering. Starving. Pigs might be eating her alive.'

'Oh God, Raewyn. No! Surely not.'

'They do, though, don't they? It happens. Either way she was dying up there, all alone, and all I could do was wait and pray. I sat in my kitchen and waited for her to walk in. Waiting, waiting, waiting. It becomes what you do, it becomes who you are. The person who waits. You can never stop. Every morning you hope that maybe, somehow, today could be the miracle day. That's why I never go away anywhere, that's why I'll never move into town, unlike every other farming widow my age. I'm still waiting for my girl to walk back in.'

She sighed, running her forefinger around the rim of her cup. I was imagining a middle-aged woman knocking on Raewyn's kitchen door. Dark curls streaked with silver, a mole on one cheek, a wide, warm smile. *Hi, Mum.*

'Midwinter always brings it back,' Raewyn was saying. 'She left on the Friday, I reported her missing on Tuesday, the twenty-first of June. The shortest day. There's something about the light, the feeling in the air. Ira and I both dread it.'

Something had set the dogs barking. Ira swore at them. He sounded angry.

'He's not happy about these media interviews.' Raewyn jerked her chin towards the door. 'He says Leah being in the papers and on the television will bring it all back.'

'And it will.'

'But what have we got to lose? I don't want to pour out my soul to some journalist, I don't want to have my photo taken, I don't want to see Leah smiling at me from every newspaper, I don't want to be gossiped about and pitied. I know people will say she only had herself to blame because she should never have gone up in that weather. We'll get horrible phone calls, and false leads, and Vince Price bailing me up—as he still does, all the time—to tell me she's in a spaceship somewhere.'

'Then why do it?'

'Because I'd give anything—*anything*—to know what happened to her. Because whatever the truth, it can't be as bad as the things I've imagined. Nothing could be worse than never knowing.'

I hoped she was right. I wasn't so sure.

TWENTY-TWO

The gunfire began at dawn. *Pop-pop-pop*. It sounded like a skirmish in some war-torn country. The fourth of May was the opening day of the duck-shooting season: how appropriate, I thought, since it was also the day my siblings were due to descend upon us.

Dad had never allowed shooting on his bit of land. Generations of ducks had worked this out, and survivors of the daily holocaust crammed themselves onto our sanctuary, calling to one another with anxious honks.

'It's bad enough if it's mallards, but paradise ducks mate for life,' Dad used to say. 'Kill one, and the other one mourns forever.'

How many people truly mate for life? I couldn't do it. My parents tried, but they couldn't either. Imagine finding your one true love, and some wannabe Rambo in camo gear shoots her down. *Pop-pop-pop*. Feathers everywhere.

Dad was as taut as a bowstring this morning. He kept asking the same questions, over and over again: *Is someone coming for lunch? Is Raewyn coming? I'm so worried—I've a feeling I invited someone for lunch.*

'Carmen and Eddie,' I reminded him. 'Just family.'

He stared into my face, his lips moving as he processed my words. 'Just family?'

'Just family. And don't worry, we're all ready. We're having cold meat and salad, and apple crumble.'

'I don't need to go shopping?'

'No need at all. Everything's ready.'

But his mind continued to torture him.

'Don't you think we should tidy up?' he persisted. 'Don't want people to think I live in a mess. We've got visitors coming, we should smarten up.'

So I gave him a duster to use on the furniture in the snug, while I made a show of plumping cushions. Five minutes later he was wringing his hands, his fingers chasing one another around his wrists.

'Someone's coming for lunch. Should we cook something?'

I showed him the meal, all stacked in the fridge. I suggested he make a pot of coffee while I nipped into the shower. That was a mistake. By the time I emerged, still wet and hurriedly pulling on clothes, the kitchen was chaos. Dad was rushing around, his lower lip stuck out in concentration, stubbornly tipping a whole cup of curry powder into a mixing bowl full of muesli. Much of the powder was flowing onto the bench. An opened can of baked beans stood nearby.

'Making a pudding,' he announced, tipping the beans into the mix.

I stood and watched with a horrified kind of fascination. I couldn't stop him, not without undermining his dignity, not without being bossy. He stirred his mixture with a wooden spoon before announcing that it should go into the fridge for a couple of hours.

'Okay!' I cried, whisking the bowl away from him. 'I'll make a space for it . . . there. Well done, Dad. Nice work.'

I somehow persuaded him to join me in a short walk, well away from the nearest shotguns. We stopped in the boot room for jackets. There were plenty hanging up on the wooden hooks, from various ages and stages of the family. Dad's was a smart hiking jacket, dark orange. I'd already adopted one of his old cast-offs.

As we strolled up the drive, the wind tugged at his white hair and made whirlpools in fallen leaves. A troupe of magpies bickered in the shelter belt, flopping and hopping and swooping. Dad stopped dead, smiling up at them.

'You and Ira were once mobbed by one of those.'

'That bird was nuts!' I cried. 'It drew blood.'

'I expect it had babies, though. And you two little hobgoblins were dancing about on the roof of Manu's woolshed, right under its nest.'

He walked on, chuckling. He looked happy and windblown, his face glowing. On impulse, I stepped closer and took his arm. It was wonderful.

•

The guns had fallen silent for the morning when Eddie's cherry-red sedan turned in at the road gate. *Sigh*. Bang on time, the deadly duo. Over the first cattle grid, past our ruined woolshed and the stand of macrocarpa. Did my brother feel even a moment's shame, I wondered, as he drove beneath our climbing tree?

Carmen was the first to throw open her door, rushing to hug me with happy shrieks. 'So good to see you! So, so good to see you!' A lifetime of riding and mucking-out had kept my sister irritatingly toned into her early fifties. She was rocking designer jeans, trendy glasses, a pixie cut in multi-layered shades of brown and bronze.

I hugged her back. Now that she was actually here, I felt warm and fuzzy towards her. Siblings, eh?

Eddie was next, making pistols with his fingers and jovially pretending to shoot me. Hilarious. He gushed about how 'fit and healthy' I looked—he meant overweight, we all knew it—and grabbed me in a bear hug.

'We have to talk about Dad,' whispered Carmen, who hadn't let go of my arm since she arrived.

As she spoke, the kitchen door slid open and Dad himself appeared, behaving like any retired father whose adult children have turned up for lunch.

'Ah! You made it,' he said. 'How was the journey?'

He was putting on his magic show again: no use of names, and asking about their journey was one-size-fits–all—he'd trotted out something very similar when I first arrived. It was a smooth performance, but he was scared to death. I could tell. I knew that immobility in his face, a look of blank truculence, like a teenager whose teacher is asking a question about the homework he hasn't done.

'Isn't it lovely that your children are all here, Dad?' I cried, trying to help him. 'Carmen, Eddie and me, back home together.'

'Indeed.' He raised his eyebrows, wiping his nose on a handkerchief before replacing it in his pocket. 'Eddie, Carmen. Well, I don't know why we're standing around. There's lunch set out on the table. French bread, salad, all kinds of good things. They've miraculously materialised, thanks to'—he smiled at me—'um, thanks to you.'

My siblings exchanged glances before following him up the steps. I stopped to pick a late rose from a bush by the drive. It was one of the old-fashioned ones and had survived both autumn temperatures and Dad's pruning frenzy. Now it was coming to its end, petals curled like soft, grasping fingers; they were deep mauve, each with a sunrise of white. I carried it inside and put it in water in a wine glass on the kitchen table.

At first we managed to behave like a nice, normal family, all together for the first time in years. You could have cut the atmosphere with a knife, but we did our best. We swapped news of our children, bringing up photos of them on our phones. Eddie showed us a cute video clip of his baby grandson's first words. Pretty soon, though, the subject of money arose—specifically, how my siblings didn't have quite enough of it. Eddie's daughter Esme was struggling to raise the deposit for a house; Carmen wanted to buy out her business partner.

By the time we came to apple crumble, Dad had stopped pretending to listen. He got up from the table and began opening random cupboards and drawers, as though hoping to find answers, or maybe somewhere to hide.

'So, Emily, what's the deal with Ira Parata?' Eddie asked, staring at me meaningfully.

I stiffened, my hackles rising. 'What about Ira?'

'I gather he's been throwing cash around. Rumour has it that he's bought himself a brand-spanking Toyota ute. He's been heard talking about a lavish European holiday. That farm's been crippled by debt ever since Manu was ill. Who d'you think is footing the bill?'

'Fake news!' I scoffed. 'You know you can't believe Tawanui gossip. Ira's rattling around in the same rust bucket he's had since the Dark Ages—no plans to change it, though I wish he would. And he desperately needs a holiday, but I don't think he's ever taken one in his life.'

'He's paying a peppercorn rent for leasing our land, isn't he?'

Oh dear. This was Eddie's best point, as I knew from the bank statements. The rent hadn't been reviewed in years, and was now about half the going rate. I'd mentioned it to Dad, who replied that the Paratas looked after him and he would never, under any circumstances, increase their rent. End of story. Apparently, Ira kept offering to pay more.

Thankfully, Dad chose that moment to interrupt the conversation.

'We'd better give our visitors some biscuits, hadn't we?' he asked, appealing to me. 'Don't want to be inhospitting. In hospital. Inhosportal. I've got biscuits somewhere.'

'He's getting worse,' muttered Eddie.

'You're making him nervous,' I muttered back, as I darted into the larder to grab the biscuits.

'I think they're in a tin of some sort,' said Dad. 'You know the one—ah!' He saw it in my hands. 'Thank you.'

Eddie got up and stood over him—much too close—as he began to stack the biscuits in a tottering pile on the table.

'Might be time we got you into St Patrick's, fella.'

'Mm?' Dad glanced up with a half-smile. 'Who?'

'St Patrick's.'

'Have a biscuit,' said Dad.

Eddie jingled keys in his pockets. His tone was casual, as though he was chatting about soccer results, but I sensed his tension. This was what they'd really come for.

'Carmen and I dropped in there and talked to the manager this morning. Holly—remember her? She's going to pull some strings, since it's you. Quite a tribute! There's a studio available right now, ready to go.'

'Ready to go where?' asked Dad.

'It really is a lovely room,' Carmen chimed in. 'Drenched in morning sun, with a very nice bathroom. You're allowed a mini fridge. They have trips out on the bus . . .'

On they went about the wonders of St Patrick's. *Dear Lord*, I thought, *please shut up*. I moved closer to Dad, resting my hand on his shoulder.

'You guys arranged a meeting this morning?' I demanded, interrupting the sales pitch. 'And you didn't think to invite Dad?'

Carmen had the grace to look guilty.

'Your life is in London, Emily. Why not use your time here to help him move? He needs professional, full-time care. He'll get a whole new lease of life once he's settled in. And we need to act fast because Holly says she can't hold this room for long. There's a waiting list.'

'He's standing right in front of you,' I snapped. 'Please stop talking about him as though he isn't here.'

Eddie swore under his breath. His lips seemed pinched, as though he had a super-sour slice of lemon on his tongue. I knew I'd got under his skin, and I couldn't resist needling him a bit more.

'You two do understand that you've got no power?' I pointed out. 'Dad's still capable of making his own decisions. But in case he can't, he's appointed me. Not you.'

'That's another thing,' snarled Eddie. 'I've taken legal advice. Those powers of attorney aren't worth the paper they're written on! Todd Tillerson has fucked up royally. Dad won't have had a clue what he was signing. He doesn't *know* you. You haven't been near him in years.'

'Is this all about protecting your inheritance? Because the longer he stays here with me, the less he'll spend on care home fees.'

Eddie was shaking his head. I was sure he and Carmen had worked out their budget in detail. He'd know exactly what the various care packages would cost.

'We can sell Arapito,' he began. 'House and land. And—'

'Sell Dad's home?'

'—distribute some capital straight away. A properly managed care plan is the only way to preserve his estate from the vultures wheeling around in the sky.'

He shot a narrow-eyed glance at me. Clearly, I was one of that flock of carrion eaters.

'Meaning me?' I asked.

'If the cap fits.'

'That's bloody insulting.'

He shrugged. 'You avoid the man for decades, and now he's got a terminal illness you've suddenly moved back home, you're being his best mate—seems a bit of a coincidence to me.'

Ting-ting. Round one. The adrenaline surged, and I came out swinging.

'Jesus Christ, Eddie, you haven't changed! You're still a bitter little loser. What must it be like, in your head? The pair of you have been talking about money since you arrived here. *You're* the vultures.'

We descended into a shouting match, a hurling of playground insults. I called Eddie a squealing piglet in the inheritance trough; he raged that I didn't give a single fuck about what was best for Felix, I'd be sodding off as soon as I got what I'd come for. Carmen was in full cry as well, telling us both to *shut* up, and *grow* up, and listen to her. Amazing how easily we all slotted back into our miserable childhood roles. Just like the good old days.

The maelstrom had reached its height when I noticed Dad's distress. He was bewildered, his mouth open, turning his head from one of us to the other.

'Shush!' I held up my hands. 'Shush, guys.'

'What are they saying?' Dad asked me. 'Who's that shouting fellow? What's made you all so cross?'

'Nothing, Dad. Sorry.'

'I don't like this. I don't like the shouting.'

He was already bashing out through the sliding door, clumsy in his haste to escape. He stumbled slightly on the porch steps before running across the lawn towards the garden shed.

I felt ashamed. Perhaps the others did too, because there was a moment's ceasefire.

'Poor old Felix,' said Eddie.

I snorted. 'You come marching in here with your jackboots, threatening to destroy the last vestiges of his autonomy. Can't you see he's terrified? Don't you care?'

'Of course I care.'

'Stop squabbling, you two,' begged Carmen. 'Please. For God's sake. Just stop.'

Dad reappeared from the shed with his spade and began digging feverishly in a flowerbed, shovelfuls of earth flying everywhere.

Eddie moved closer to the window, watching him. 'I really do care,' he said.

'I know you do,' murmured Carmen.

We all watched Dad for another minute, before Eddie announced that he was going for a walk, and stepped outside. Carmen tutted sadly as her twin wandered off across the paddock with his head down, his hands in his pockets.

'You need to cut Eddie a bit of slack,' she said. 'He's hurting. He's losing his father. And Dad choosing to trust you with the powers of attorney, not us—that was a real slap in the face.'

'Why d'you never take my side?'

'It isn't a question of sides.'

'Ever since Eddie shook me out of that bloody tree, and you lied about it.'

'You're not still on about that tree, are you?' She smiled incredulously at me. 'How old were you? Eight? Ten? You guys were always squabbling. It never, ever stopped. You had a sharp tongue, you ran rings around Eddie, and he used to lose his temper. I had more sense than to get involved.'

'I know it was about forty years ago, and we've all got grey hairs now—'

'Speak for yourself!' she chuckled, patting her head. 'Honey highlights and balayage, according to my hairdresser.'

'This isn't funny.'

'Look . . .' She'd stopped smiling. 'Eddie was an unhappy kid, and a bit of an idiot, and he did a stupid thing in the heat of the moment. But he regretted it straight away; he was hysterical after you fell.'

'He's never once apologised.'

'Surely you can let it go now, after all this time? It doesn't matter.'

Doesn't matter! The child in me wanted to rage that I'd never forgotten the terror, that my brain took years to recover, that it may have changed the whole trajectory of my life—and, worst of all, that nobody seemed to care.

'Eddie was always the squeaky wheel, wasn't he?' Carmen was saying. 'Mum thought we emigrated at a bad time for him— a difficult kid at a gawky stage. You were jolly and fun and popular, thick as thieves with Ira. I had lots of friends at school. Eddie didn't have any. Leah only tolerated him. People didn't like him. They were mean. They wouldn't come to our birthday parties, or invite him to theirs. Even our parents weren't there for him—Dad never at home, Mum struggling. In the end, Eddie got bitter. And yes, for a while he wasn't a very nice person.'

She'd hit a nerve. Nathan went through a friendless patch too. Almost nobody came to his tenth birthday party. Broke both our hearts.

'None of that justifies shaking me out of a tree, or you lying about it,' I huffed, but I could hear how petty I sounded.

'I didn't really lie. I just minimised. I felt sorry for him. He's my twin, and if I hadn't stood up for him, the whole town would have been calling him a psycho. His life would have got even worse.'

For the second time in ten minutes, I felt ashamed. I remembered Brad Taylor and Greta Miller the night we went to the cinema; how casually vicious we all were about Eddie. I encouraged them. I even gave them ammunition.

Dad had moved to another flowerbed. Another hole, another mound of soil.

'What the hell is he doing?' asked Carmen.

'He just digs and digs.'

'Eddie shouldn't have called you a vulture,' she said. 'But we truly don't understand why you'd want to be stuck way out here. After all these years, why would you suddenly turn up now?'

'If I don't help Dad, he can't stay in his own home. That's it. That's my agenda. I don't know how long I can manage, but I'm prepared to try for a while. I'm paying my own way, don't worry.'

'Okay.' She nodded, smoothing her jeans with one hand. 'I'll talk to Eddie.'

'Are you really going to challenge the powers of attorney?'

'What would be the point?'

I put the kettle on, trying to think of a change of subject.

'I'm using your room as a studio,' I said, with a flash of inspiration. 'D'you want to come and take a look?'

It was the first time I'd ever shared my working life with my sister. I showed her the text, the storyboard, tracings, detailed drawings and the finished versions. I explained how it all worked.

'I had no idea the process was so complicated,' she said, stooping over my work-in-progress. 'It's clever, really, isn't it?'

She was doing her lukewarm best. Nan Kirkland's terror of instilling vanity in her children had rippled down the generations. While she was distracted by the Christmas kitten, I slipped across to the wardrobe.

'This yours?' I asked casually, dropping the turquoise beanie into her hands.

I'd been looking for an opportunity to ambush her. After all, I'd found the beanie among some of her things. If she had a guilty secret involving Leah, now was the time she might betray herself.

She turned it around. Mild interest, no more.

'Nah, not mine . . . garish colour, isn't it? I vaguely remember digging this out of Dad's room. I was going to borrow it, but Richard gave me one of his to wear.'

'D'you think it was Mum's?'

'Maybe. It's a bit lurid for Dad. Lots of holes in it—look.' Her finger poked through the fabric. 'Moths.'

'I'll chuck it out,' I said, and returned it to the wardrobe.

Carmen had sat down on the bed, leaning back on her hands and gazing around the room. 'Do you remember us getting ready in here, on my wedding day?'

We both smiled at the memory. We'd opened a bottle of bubbly and pranced about to the soundtrack from *Grease*. Mum did our hair with the same electric rollers that were now languishing in the cupboard.

'Dad has a collection of souvenirs from all our childhoods,' I said. 'Did you know? They're in Bert's army chest. Pictures, certificates and things. He's got the order of service from your wedding.'

'In Bert's chest?'

'In a box with your name on it. Next time you come, ask to have a look.'

'Huh! Dad.' Carmen looked pleased. She glanced out of the window, towards where he was still digging. 'Tell you a secret. He broke down in the wedding car. He looked so handsome, so smart, but he was always like a bloody automaton—d'you know what I mean?'

'I do.'

'Well, he was human that day. He said he'd been a disastrous husband, so he was the last person to give me any advice. *I just long for you to be happy! Please be happy!* Then he burst into tears.'

'Actual tears?'

'Yep, he was a mess. I had to ask the driver to go around the block about five times. Remember I was late? To be fair, Mum was blubbing too.'

We watched Dad shove his foot onto the spade, jumping to drive it deep into the earth, hurling it out again. I was thinking about that photo of Leah in the green box. *I love you. We love one another.*

'That was the last time I ever saw Leah,' said Carmen.

I was startled to hear Leah's name, just as she was on my own mind.

'She caught your bouquet,' I said.

'And gave it to someone else. She said she wasn't the marrying kind.' Carmen sighed. 'And as it turned out, she was right.'

·

I called Nathan that night. He and Ella were back in Jakarta. He was loving the work, the people, the city; Ella, apparently, was not. She'd suffered through a bout of food poisoning.

'So she might pack up and head home?' I asked hopefully, and he guffawed.

'You just wish.'

'I don't dislike Ella.'

'No, Mum, 'course you don't dislike her. You just wish she'd sod off.'

My son has an uncannily accurate bullshit detector; nothing gets past him. He asked about what he called 'the invasion of the sibling horde'. I told him we'd had a bust-up and upset Dad, and Eddie stormed off for a walk by himself.

'Awkward,' said Nathan. 'So have you and Eddie spoken since?'

'We have indeed,' I said. 'He came back from his walk and I was nice to him.' We'd all had an excruciating cup of tea, talking about the weather as though nothing had happened. Under-carpet-sweeping.

'So Grandpa won't be moving into a home?'

'Not at the moment. Not while I'm living here, at least.'

'Nice one, Mum! You repelled all boarders.'

'They really seemed to believe I'm only here to get my hands on his money. You'd think he was a billionaire, the way they go on.'

'Hm.' I imagined Nathan pushing his glasses up his nose, blinking. 'I don't think this is about money. I reckon they're jealous.'

'I'm quite sure they aren't. I'm the family black sheep.'

'They'd never admit it. The thing is, you all moan about Grandpa, all three of you, and Grandma's just as bad. You've all got this theme that he had more time for his patients than he did for you. But you all kind of worship him too. You want his approval.'

'We do not!'

''Course you do. And now you're the prodigal daughter. Fatted calf, rejoicing. You can bet your socks they're jealous.'

I rather liked this theory.

'Thanks,' I said. 'I'll take that.'

I came very close to asking his advice about the beanie in the cupboard, the contents of the box marked *HER*. Perhaps he'd have some new perspective on those as well.

'Funny thing . . .' I began. And then I stopped.

'Funny thing?' he prompted.

'Gone clear out of my mind. Sorry. Middle-aged brain.'

Some things are better left unsaid. Or even unthought.

TWENTY-THREE

We were still recovering from the twins' visit when, a few days later, a southerly storm swept up the east coast, coming straight from the Antarctic. Ira's stock turned their backs to the horizontal rain, pressing against the fences in huddles of misery. The weather people—MetService—were forecasting snow on high ground.

That night, I drew all the curtains and made myself and Dad two hot-water bottles each. Gusts battered the wooden structure of the house; the wallpaper seemed to breathe and stir. The windows rattled.

I was rattling too, as I lurched in and out of sleep. Leah was dripping wet, water streaming out of her hair. She mentioned Eddie's name, and Ira's, and even Todd's. She talked about the three hunters in their truck, but I couldn't hear her properly because of the pounding of gunfire on the roof. None of it made any sense.

She held up a bar of Cadbury's. 'Got a craving,' she said.

'Craving for what?'

'This should keep me going all the way to Biddulph's.'

That was when I saw the blackberry smudges across her jaw, her nose, around both eyes. She looked as though someone had taken a baseball bat to her face.

'What happened, Leah?' I asked. 'Who did that to you?'

A door slammed somewhere in the house, making my own eyes snap open. Pitch-blackness. Dad was crying continuously, as an animal will cry, with falsetto moans. '*Helen? Helen!*'

It was the third night in a row, and I was beginning to fray at the edges. For the hundredth time I imagined him safe in a centrally heated room at St Patrick's, with pressure pad alarms and night staff on call. I had to drag myself out from under the duvet, fumbling for warm clothes.

He stood in the icy corridor, a lamenting ghost in a hell of his own.

'Oh dear, Dad,' I said wearily. 'Nightmares again?'

I took his arm and coaxed him to lie down in the snug. I'd taken to keeping a pillow and soft blankets ready on the sofa for just this purpose.

'She's still up there,' he told me, as I spread the blankets over him.

'Helen?'

'Helen? No! Helen's buried in a cemetery in Leeds. Leah's up there.' His face crumpled, as though he'd only just heard the news. 'It's so awful. She's covered in snow. She'll be so cold.'

'I think that was what you said when they called off the search. D'you remember, Dad? But it was a long, long time ago. She won't be feeling the cold anymore.'

What a stupid thing for me to say. It had him in tears. I fetched a box of tissues, gave him a squeeze on the shoulder—*almost* a hug. I made a show of messing about with the stove, clattering the poker, blowing embers into life. The next time I checked, his eyes were closed.

I looked through the bookcase for something comforting,

chose *All Creatures Great and Small*, and curled up in the armchair near the stove. But I couldn't read. Not a word.

She's covered in snow. She'll be so cold.

Something was creeping through my mind, spreading a monstrous darkness. *You're just tired*, I told myself. *This means nothing. After all, she is still up there. And what's left of her— if anything—probably will be covered in snow. That's all he means. That's all he means.*

Nathan said something similar once, about our puppy. Patsy. She brought us such joy, but one day she slipped her collar and ran under the wheels of a bus. My little chap was about nine. He sat and wailed, his shoulders sagging like an old man's. *Patsy will be lonely without us! We can't put her in the ground! She'll be cold.*

I wished Nathan were here with me now. I sent him a Facebook message—*Hi, how's life in Jakarta today?*—and was cheered when a reply jumped onto my phone with a chirpy *ting*: a photo of him, in a classroom with his students. I was comforted to think of my son living his life, far away from this looking-glass world. He couldn't begin to put himself in my shoes: middle-aged, awake in the darkest hours of the night, watching my father die in super-slow motion.

Another message came through.

What u doing awake FFS? It must be about 4 am!!
Grandpa's getting worse. He woke me up again.
Sorry. Poor Grandpa ☹
When I lose my marbles, I'll move in with you and your third wife!
No you won't. I'll stick you in a home
Charming!
So what's he doing? How does he wake you up?
He wanders around all night, talking rubbish and wailing
Like Lady Macbeth?

Exactly like her
Bloody hands!
Alzheimer's is a bugger. Not for the faint-hearted.
*Out damned spot! Lady M had a dog called Spot, did you
know?*

I felt lighter after this silly conversation. Once we'd signed off, I closed my eyes. I never noticed the wind dropping, the rain passing on, the darkness paling. I woke to find myself still in the armchair with James Herriot open on my lap, Gyp and Gloria in a snuffling pile on the sofa. Dad must have taken himself back to bed.

I made myself coffee, toast and marmalade before tiptoeing out onto the porch to be greeted by a slap-in-the-face of icy air. The night's storm had left beauty in its wake: the first snow. Just a dusting on the uplands, catching the glitter of dawn. For a moment I stood, enchanted—but then I was swearing and leaping down the porch steps, because I'd spotted Dad out there: barefoot, wearing nothing but his striped pyjamas while driving his spade into a heavily frosted vegetable patch.

'Hey!' I cried, galloping across to him. 'What on earth d'you think you're doing?'

He watched me mutely, rubbing his nose with the back of his wrist. His hands and feet had turned a bruised, purplish blue. The same disturbing colour rimmed his lips, while the rest of his face was a bloodless white. He could have played the drowned corpse in a horror film, except that he was shivering violently.

'You'll catch your death!' I scolded, taking the spade out of his hand.

'Hope so.'

I bribed him with promises of toast and coffee as I ushered him inside. He sat and teeth-chattered by the stove while I piled rugs and hot-water bottles all over him. I noticed that his toenails badly needed cutting, so I fetched a pair of nail scissors and clipped them. Never in my whole life had I touched my father's feet. I thought he'd be embarrassed, but he just twiddled his toes, as though pleased I was taking care of him.

'I can't feel them at all,' he said, smiling. 'Have they dropped off?'

'You're asking to die of hypothermia!'

'Interesting phenomenon, hypothermia. D'you know how it works?'

While I rubbed life into his frozen extremities, he delivered a lecture on the physiology of extreme cold. He must have accessed the right file in his memory bank because knowledge came tumbling out. He told me what temperature a human body would normally be, what temperature it might be at each stage of hypothermia, and what physical effect all of this would have. He described finding a climber who was sliding into the final stages.

'We followed a trail of clothes,' he said, his blue eyes wide with bemused wonder. 'Her gloves, her hat, jacket, even her socks . . . she was tearing them off, you see, and discarding them. It's sometimes called paradoxical undressing, and it certainly *is* paradoxical, in sub-zero temperatures. She thought she was hot! Quite often, in the final stages, people find a nook or cranny and crawl in there to die. A burrowing instinct.'

'Had she done that?'

'Not yet. We found her just in time—*just* in time: we nearly lost her while we were carrying her down to the helicopter. But she wasn't unhappy. In fact, I'd describe her as euphoric. She kept asking us to leave her in peace, let her go to sleep.'

'I'd be petrified.'

'You might not. People who've suffered hypothermia sometimes talk about feeling a kind of bliss.' He stared thoughtfully at his numb toes. 'Of all the ways to go, it's not the worst one.'

I remembered Dave Perry all those years ago, trying to reassure Raewyn. *She'd probably just fall asleep.*

'Not my first choice,' I said.

'We don't all get to choose.'

•

That afternoon, I was in the butcher's shop when Todd Tillerson walked past the window, spotted me and waved. As I stepped out into the pale sunshine, he was waiting.

'In mufti today?' I asked, glancing at his jeans and padded jacket.

'It's Saturday.' He peered at me. 'For Christ's sake, Emily Kirkland—no offence, but you look bloody awful.'

'Bit tired,' I admitted. 'Weird, weird night.'

'You need coffee.'

I'd left Dad with Raewyn, who'd dropped in to deliver the parish newsletter, took one look at me—yawning, my hair unbrushed—and told me to take a break. She and Dad would be putting pea hay down in the garden. *Shoo!* she insisted, when I hesitated. *Go!*

'How's Dr Kirkland doing?' asked Todd, as we headed up the sunny side of the street.

People asked me that question all the time, and my answer was generally a lie. 'Pretty well,' I'd say, or, 'We're getting there'— which is surely one of the most meaningless platitudes in the English language. Getting *where*, for God's sake? We certainly weren't getting anywhere good.

Todd was different. He knew.

'I lie in bed at night,' I said, 'and I listen to him crying.'

'Why's he crying?'

'He's lost. Sometimes he says things . . . He calls for his sister.'

'I didn't know he had a sister. Is she in Yorkshire?'

He looked quite shaken when I told him the story of Helen's short life.

'You never know what people have lived through, do you?' he said.

Forty Degrees was packed, so we chose a table out on the pavement. It was slightly too cold for comfort. The Ruahines dominated the horizon, bright shards of ice with blue-bruise shadows.

'I heard a rumour,' said Todd, after Chouma brought our coffee. 'The media are going to rehash Leah's disappearance.'

I sighed. 'Yup. We'll be back in the news. *A town haunted by grief*. Raewyn still hopes to find out what happened to her. Ira thinks it's going to be too painful.'

'He might have a point.'

A farmer stopped to ask about subdividing his land. Todd was polite, gave him five minutes of free advice. Life for a small-town lawyer, I supposed. Same as for the doctor. Nowhere to hide.

Once we were alone again, he squinted up at the sky. It was high and pure, with a fine patina of silver.

'Great day for flying. Want to come?'

'Today? Now?'

'Why not?'

'Oh! So, *so* tempting.'

I hadn't been up in a light aircraft since I bought a birthday flight for Nathan and a friend. I went too, and loved it even more than the boys did.

'We'll be back before you know it,' cajoled Todd. 'C'mon, who wouldn't want to be up there, on this glorious day?'

•

Raewyn answered our house phone. After assuring me that all was well, she handed it over to Dad.

'Flying!' he exclaimed. 'How marvellous.'

'I'll be back by three. Got sausages for dinner. Plenty for Raewyn too, if she'd like to stay?'

'Right you are.'

I heard Raewyn's voice in the background.

'She says to tell Todd to fly over the garden,' said Dad. 'We'll look out for you.'

•

The sign proclaimed that this was *Tawanui Aeroclub—Learn to Fly*, with an illustration of a tiny biplane looping the loop around the words. There wasn't much to it: just a paddock, a clubhouse, a hangar and a windsock. Several aircraft were parked on the grass, and a couple of middle-aged guys stood with arms folded, chatting affably. Tawanui people spent a lot of time doing that.

Todd walked around his Cessna, checking things, and then we were off, no messing about. Moments after we'd clambered into the tiny cockpit, the propeller began to turn.

I'd forgotten just how much racket a light aircraft makes when taking off, or how ridiculously unstable it feels when the wheels first leave the ground. We yawed, bucked, juddered—and then I found myself grinning as we banked sharply and began to gain height, flying over the town, up into the silvery emptiness. Soon we were following the glinting twists of the Arapito stream as it wound across farmland, gullies filled with scrub, skeins of native bush.

Todd's voice crackled into my earphones. 'See your dad?'

I was staring through the scratched perspex. It took me several seconds to work out that those toy buildings ahead, tucked neatly into the folds of the land, were the place where I grew up. The landscape of my childhood was laid out: our house, the front paddock, the school bus shelter. A lone figure in the garden, white-haired. A flash of sunlight on his spade.

'There he is!' I yelled, but the engine was so loud that I couldn't hear my own voice.

The figure began to wave both arms in wide sweeps; Todd waggled our wings in reply. The shadow of the Cessna darted across the roof of the house just as I glimpsed Raewyn on the porch. When I craned my neck to look back, Dad was still waving and waving. He looked so small.

Seconds later we'd swept over Ira's cabin, across the Arapito ravine—and there was Biddulph Road. I hadn't appreciated how close to our place it passed, as the Cessna flies. We followed the meandering track through the foothills, though at times it was smothered by native bush. I spotted several places where it crossed mountain streams. And then, abruptly, it ended.

'Was this where they found Leah's car?' I asked, and Todd nodded.

Such a godforsaken spot. There was often a small parking area at the start of hiking trails; sometimes a picnic table, a trail map, perhaps a long-drop toilet. As a teenager I'd spent many a happy hour in picnic spots like that. My mates and I called it 'camping', but it wasn't half so wholesome as the word suggests. We'd pile into cars, hoon out there and party—which involved drinking and smoking whatever we could get our hands on, dancing on the table. I lost my virginity in one of those car parks. Lots of people did.

But Biddulph Road simply ended, and the bush began—an all-encompassing wave, drowning any sign of human life. As we gained height, I was reminded of the TV footage from the search for Leah. I couldn't see any hint of a trail beneath the peaks and troughs of that ocean, the misted shadows and glowing patches of sunlight. Beautiful, yes, but unspeakably lonely.

High on the tree line, Todd pointed to a tiny structure. It looked as though it had grown there, like a mushroom. Biddulph's bivvy. Beyond it stretched the uplands, tussock grasslands frosted with snow. We traced Leah's route along a rocky knife-edge. It would be so easy to slip, wouldn't it? In rain and cloud, with gusts of wind that might lift a person off her feet.

Finally we turned west and droned over still more track-less wilderness, ridge after featureless ridge, clothed in dense rainforest. Neither of us spoke for a long time. I was feeling over-whelmed at the thought of being lost in that crumpled expanse. The sun was distorted, a white star on the horizon.

Todd's voice sounded harsh through the headset. 'Beyond forty degrees south, there is no law.'

'Beyond fifty,' I added, 'there is no God.'

I saw him smile. Then he began a long turn, and we headed back to humanity.

TWENTY-FOUR

A creak. A click—the bolt on the bathroom door. It had sounded exactly the same for forty years.

Not again, I thought miserably. *Not again, please: make it stop.* I felt as though I'd been run over by a ten-tonne truck. I was tired of being calm and jolly in the face of this implacable disintegration.

It was *so* cold out there, and my bed was *so* warm. Temperatures had dropped dramatically since that first fall of snow on the mountains. I'd shopped for sheepskin slippers, a possum-wool bobble cap and fingerless gloves. As I let Gloria and Gyp out onto the frosty lawn in the mornings, my breath turned into the pale puff of a ghost. Carmen's room had an open fire. I'd taken to lighting it first thing, thinking longingly of radiators and central heating.

The bathroom door again. I heard Dad roaming all over the house, and then his voice. 'God forgive me. God forgive me.'

As I padded wearily down the corridor, I swear I felt frost rising through the floorboards. A lamp was on in the snug, the fire still glowing from the evening before. Dad was facing away from me, leaning forwards in the armchair with his hand on Gloria's head.

'Forgive me.' He sounded slurred, the drunk uncle at a family wedding. 'Forgive me. I'll never forgive myself.'

I was about to make my presence known when he said something else. Something much worse.

'I . . . I . . .' His voice broke. He gave several heaving, dry sobs before forcing out the words. 'I killed her.'

I stood stock-still in the archway. I don't think I was breathing.

'I left you up there,' he said. 'You're still up there, because I—'

Enough. I ran in, prattling nonsense at top volume, anything to stop him talking.

'I killed her!' he cried, looking up at me. His hair was crazy, eyes red-rimmed.

'No, Dad! It's not real. You've had a nightmare.'

'I have to tell Raewyn.'

'It was a dream.' I was desperate to erase what I'd just heard. 'Okay? Okay, Dad? Just a dream.'

I kneeled down on the floor beside him, taking both his hands. They were so cold, so much smaller than I remembered. Everything about him was smaller than I remembered.

'I'm a killer,' he whispered. 'I'm a—I'm a—I'm a coward.'

'Shush, shush. Just a dream.'

He rambled on and on, repeating the same terrible nonsense between his sobs.

'I left her up there. She's still up there. I killed her, I left her up there. Coward, you see . . .'

I put my arms around him, hugging him properly for the first time I could ever remember, shushing and tutting. Dear old Gloria nuzzled his hands with her nose. I'm sure she was trying to comfort him too.

When at last he seemed calmer, I turned away to stoke the fire. I was close to tears myself. All my life this man had been bloodless and unmovable, carved out of granite. I'd often wished he was a different kind of father, but he was one of *my* waymarks. Now the granite was dissolving. I felt lost.

The next time I looked around, he was sitting on the edge of the armchair, his gaze fixed on the silent flames behind the glass door of the stove. His expression had grown vacant again, his eyes sagging and watery. Both dogs were butting their heads against him now, making the most of his warmth and company in the early hours.

I was startled when he suddenly laughed. Gloria had rolled onto her back and was holding up all four paws.

'Funny old girl,' he murmured, rubbing her biscuit-golden stomach.

The grandmother clock whirred, *click-click-click*, before chiming three. Dad cocked his head, his eyebrows raised.

'Good Lord. Is that three in the afternoon, or the morning?'

'The morning.'

'So late!'

'Very late.'

'I'm not sure what you're doing here. Are you staying?' he asked, getting to his feet.

'I am, Dad.'

'Well, do you know where you're sleeping? You do? Excellent. Goodnight.'

He was already wandering away to his room. Moments later, I heard his door shut.

I didn't go back to bed. I was afraid of my raging thoughts, in all that silence and dark. The snug at least had firelight, and the dogs for company. I sat and stared at the wall. Cobwebs. Cracks. Years and years of fly and spider dirt.

The permafrost was thawing. Prehistoric creatures were emerging from the tundra. A young mammoth, dead in the ice for forty thousand years.

I killed her.

Of course he didn't kill her. Leah had a hiking accident. Poor visibility, high winds.

She's covered in snow. She'll be so cold.

I tore the packaging off my memories. He was certainly in this house when Raewyn raised the alarm. I saw him myself, answering the phone. But what about the days in between, after Leah set out? Where was he then?

It was too long ago. I couldn't remember.

Think. Think. Who was at home?

Carmen was on her honeymoon. Mum and Eddie were here.

And Dad? He used to spend very little time in the house, even less while Mum was staying. He'd work at the surgery all day before beginning home visits, paperwork and meetings. He travelled to conferences around the country. He led training exercises with the search and rescue volunteers. He quite often slept at the hospice, especially if someone was nearing the end of their life.

Hang on, though. Hang on. Dad had a winter bug, didn't he? Yes, he did! Spent the weekend comatose in bed, looking bloody awful. Mum scoffed about his man flu. We heard him throwing up. I saw him myself, when I tiptoed into his room to offer a bowl of soup, a cup of tea.

I punched the air, light-headed with relief. Hooray! I was my father's alibi!

I should have stopped there. I should have poured myself a stiff whisky and got stuck into a good book or—much better still—gone back to sleep. I absolutely should *not* have carried on running over the events of those few days.

Start again. Engage memory banks. Let's make sure.

Leah left on the Friday. She spoke to me at the petrol station, on her way to Biddulph Road.

Okay.

But I didn't go home that night, did I? No. I went to see *Jurassic Park* and woke up tangled in Brad Taylor's revolting sheets. I drove straight from there to work. By Saturday afternoon, Dad was prostrate in his room, shivering with fever. But I couldn't be one hundred per cent sure, couldn't swear in court, that he was home all of Friday night.

I killed her.

•

'Bloody hell,' said Sarah.

She phoned in the morning, wanting to talk about a very exciting new project: Admiral Flufflebum SNAP! cards. I wanted to talk about Dad.

I'd eventually fallen asleep on the sofa in the snug, and woken to find him returning from a stroll with the dogs. He insisted that he'd slept very well, all night. 'Like a baby', he said.

Sarah's call caught me at a bad moment. I was running on coffee and adrenaline, skittish with panic. I walked fast up the drive, spilling out my story. 'I wish I hadn't heard him,' I moaned.

'I bet. You sound quite shaken. What're you going to do?'

Good question. What do you do when your father confesses to murder? There's no flowchart for a situation like this.

'I have to tell Ira and Raewyn, don't I?'

'Hang on a bit, let's take this apart,' reasoned Sarah. 'The poor man's got Alzheimer's, right? We all know that's a godawful thing. My grandmother had something similar, and she decided she'd lost a little boy. She'd rush about looking for him—*Have you seen my son? I've lost my son.* The thing is, Granny never even had a son. The kid was a figment of her imagination. Could it be the same with your dad? A false memory?'

'He does have delusions. Sometimes he thinks he's being kept prisoner, and I'm an evil jailer or something.'

It was evening in England. I heard the glug of a nightcap being poured.

'Say hello to our future,' Sarah said gloomily. 'I've started forgetting things already. I tell myself it's my hormones.'

I'd reached the school bus shelter. This tiny wooden structure was already here when our family moved into Arapito. I used to huddle on the seat in the early mornings, marvelling at frost-glittering spiderwebs. Nobody used it anymore, except for the birds. I counted five empty nests tucked under the eaves.

'Do you . . .' Sarah's voice became distorted before fading away. Phone reception was always patchy at this end of the drive. I moved to the far side of the shelter, and she reappeared '. . . even remotely possible that he hurt Leah? You know your own father.'

'I'm not sure I do. I thought I did, before I found that box by his bed.'

'From what you've told me, he's a supremely self-disciplined man who has spent his entire career working tirelessly to save lives. Right? He's also very close friends with her mother. Even if he and Leah had an affair—and that's a big if—it's hardly in character, is it, for him to lure her to an isolated spot and throttle her—or knife her—or whatever?'

'Definitely out of character,' I said, sitting down on the bench. *Then again*, I thought, *he's good at keeping up an act. His magic trick. He does it every day.*

'The most likely explanation, by far, is that this memory is a symptom of his disease,' declared Sarah. 'It's a living nightmare for him, but it's in his head. I'd forget all about it, if I were you.'

She was right. She *had* to be right. Dad's mind was playing cruel tricks. I began to see the glimmer of an explanation: as a child he was taught to hate himself, to feel constant guilt. If he and Leah had some kind of relationship, that would surely exacerbate his guilt. And, finally, he'd failed to rescue her when she got into trouble in the mountains. Failure, self-hatred, guilt. He blamed himself for her death; he felt as though he'd killed her himself. All of this had surfaced now that his mind was dissolving.

I explained my pop-psychology theory to Sarah, who enthu-siastically ran with it.

'The other night,' I told her, 'he was obsessing about how Leah will be covered in snow. He kept saying it: *covered in snow.* Those were his exact words when they called off the search.'

'Oh, the poor man! He's stuck in that traumatic moment.'

'What if he starts confessing to other people? If anyone else heard him last night, the police would've shown up by now. Imagine what that would do to him.'

A cold gust reached into the bus shelter, scattering dry leaves.

'Can't happen,' said Sarah. 'Mustn't happen. Don't let it happen.'

And that's how I gained a new mission in life: to keep my father from confessing to a murder.

TWENTY-FIVE

I didn't recognise the phone number, nor the friendly voice with the Irish accent, nor the name: Niamh something-or-other, a freelance journalist.

'I'm writing a feature about Leah Parata,' she began. 'It'll appear in *The Courier* and its sister papers, and online. I understand you were the last person to speak to her. I wonder if you'd be okay to meet up for a chat?'

This was, officially, the first day of winter: 1 June. I was standing on the porch. Flocks of goldfinches and sparrows bounced around the frosted lawn while Dad scattered seed for them.

'All I did was sell her a bar of chocolate,' I said. 'It was a very long time ago.'

'Still, you're a piece in the jigsaw.'

I was racking my brains for an excuse. Since Dad's confession, I'd tried to turn the house into an isolation unit. I rarely left him alone, apart from anxious dashes to the shops. I was on tenterhooks every time anyone dropped by, especially Raewyn or Ira. When he was invited to a fundraising concert at the hospice, I drove him and hovered within earshot, ready to intervene. I insisted on being his support person at the dentist. I cut his hair myself, much to his amusement. I also developed a crashing neck ache that wouldn't go away, no matter how many ibuprofen I took.

My old friend Admiral Flufflebum was saving my sanity, with the help of George the ginger kitten: frightened and bedraggled, hiding in a manger, warmed by military horses, fed by white-hatted palace chefs. Every morning I switched on the radio, filling Carmen's room with music, and escaped into colour and texture and light.

'Just a chat,' wheedled Niamh. 'We could be done and dusted in half an hour.'

No, no!

'Of course,' I said. 'Happy to help.'

•

Forty Degrees smelled of warm scones. We sat in a corner with a recording device on the table between us. Tea for Niamh, coffee for me.

The journalist turned out to be about my own age and reassuringly scruffy: denim jacket, bitten fingernails. She was originally from Donegal but 'met some Kiwi guy' and ended up here. She claimed to have been looking at some of my illustrations online.

'They're gorgeous,' she said. 'So much life.'

I'm sure this was just flattery, but I found her accent mesmeric. Perhaps that was how she got people to talk.

'So,' she began, 'Leah Parata. What was she like?'

I did my best to describe the Leah I knew, to say things that would make Raewyn happy if they appeared in print. *She was passionate about conservation. She was incredibly clever. She was a black belt at judo, did you know that?* I talked about her coming to feed our eel, and how she knew all about its life cycle. I mentioned how hard-working she was; how charged with energy, but at the same time poised and self-contained.

'Boyfriends?'

'At the time she disappeared, you mean? Nobody local; I don't
know about in Wellington. There was no shortage of hopefuls,
including my brother.' I clapped a hand to my mouth. 'God,
I shouldn't have . . . Please don't quote me on that—it's off the
record, right?'

Niamh smiled. 'Off the record. I won't be dropping you in
any trouble.'

That bloody voice recorder was unnerving. I imagined her
replaying the conversation, listening to every nuance through a
set of headphones, picking up the tinniness of a false note. I had
nothing to hide. Nothing, except the fact that my demented father
seemed to think he'd killed Leah, along with the small matter of
his possessing a photo of her, and a beanie disturbingly like the
one she was wearing when she disappeared, and a stash of love
letters from someone who signed themselves 'L'.

Niamh had tracked down the police officer who headed the
investigation. He'd retired long ago, but never considered the case
to be closed.

'He still wonders about Leah,' she told me. 'It's haunted him.'

'It's haunted us all.'

She was pouring milk into her tea. 'Her brother won't talk
to me.'

'I'm not surprised. He's never got over it.'

She acknowledged Ira's grief with a grimace, then continued,
'Could you tell me about that last conversation with her? The bar
of chocolate.'

I began to recount those five minutes of my life, minutes that
I longed to go back and change. Low cloud, drifting rain. Leah in
her waterproof jacket and hiking boots with red laces.

'What did you talk about?' asked Niamh.

'Um . . . it was such a long time ago, I can't remember every . . .
we certainly talked about the weather. She seemed to think the

rain was a bonus because it would make her snails easier to find. She loved those snails.'

'Did *you* think she was wise to be going up there?'

I was afraid the question might be a trap. I wasn't going to be drawn into any kind of criticism.

'Leah was no rookie,' I said. 'She was well-equipped, experienced, super-fit. She'd checked the forecast. She knew the country, she knew her bushcraft. She was Dr Parata! You have to remember that. Everyone looked up to her.'

'That's what I keep hearing. You too?'

'Of course.' I cast a glance at the recorder and said it again, with even more enthusiasm. 'Of *course*.'

'Hang on now.' Niamh had got out her notebook. She turned pages, laid her finger on one of the lines. 'There was mention of some injuries. Bruises, a black eye. People in Wellington saw them.'

'She fell down some steps after colliding with someone.'

'You didn't spot anything like that?'

'No.' I put my jacket on top of the recorder and leaned closer, dropping my voice. 'Please, please don't put this in your article, but I think people clung to all kinds of crazy rumours, because they didn't want to believe that Leah made a mistake. They had her on a pedestal. Turns out she was human.'

Niamh wrinkled her nose, pressing down with her hands to show me she'd got the point.

'What effect did her disappearance have?' she asked, moving my jacket away from the recorder. 'I mean, on the community?'

'It spread a shadow over us all. Everyone knows everyone here. Most of 'em are related—and Leah was a Tawanui woman, born and bred. Her father, Manu Parata, had just died horribly. It was the second tragedy to strike the family in as many years.'

'So sad,' murmured Niamh.

I was beginning to relax. This wasn't a journalistic bloodhound who'd catch the scent of a scandal at fifty paces and rip our lives apart. She was after a human-interest story.

She turned another page of her notebook.

'Dr Felix Kirkland,' she said. 'Your father, right? He led the search.'

I froze, mid-sip.

'He . . .' I forced myself to breathe. 'No, he wasn't the coordinator, but he sounded the alarm. He was a search and rescue volunteer, so Raewyn called him when Leah was overdue. He and Ira ran straight up to Biddulph's bivvy. They found Leah's log.'

Niamh knew all this. She was nodding rapidly. 'I've managed to get hold of a copy of that log,' she announced, pulling a document out of her bag and laying it in front of me. 'I don't think it's ever been published before. Have you seen it?'

I had, though not for decades. I glanced at the photocopy, rolling my mug between my palms.

A single, ruled page, covered in scrawled handwriting. Some of the words were obscured by a dark coffee ring, perhaps from Leah's last-ever cup. I already knew what she'd written. It was poignant to think of her sitting at the packing-case table in the bivvy with her cup of coffee, calmly documenting what would turn out to be her own death.

As I focused on that writing, a warning klaxon blared in my mind.

Blue biro. Angular, sloping forwards. Leah's handwriting.

Leah's handwriting.

Leah's handwriting.

'Upsetting, isn't it?' Niamh was looking at me. 'Her last words. She seems so upbeat, too.'

The sight of that log finally brought my head out of the sand. It was as though Leah was reaching out to me, desperately trying to tell me what had happened to her.

'I'm sorry, Niamh,' I said, pushing the photocopy back towards her. 'I think I'd better run. I've left Dad alone.'

'I'd really like to talk to Dr Kirkland.'

Horrifying suggestion. I knocked back the last of my coffee, splashing brown drops onto my sleeve.

'He couldn't possibly help you. There's no point.'

'I know he's—'

'Alzheimer's. It would only upset him.'

I made a show of being distracted by the spill. There was no way I could let this woman, with her disarming smile and lilting accent, talk to Dad about Leah. God only knew what confessions he might pour into her sympathetic ear.

She pulled a wodge of serviettes out of their dispenser, and passed them to me. 'If you mop that now, it'll be a lot less trouble down the track. Easier to wash.'

'He can't remember anything,' I said, dabbing at the accusing spots. 'He makes mistakes, he gets frustrated. I mean . . . I don't mean he has a temper. Not at all.'

I risked another glance at Leah's handwriting. *Yes. Yes.* I'd seen those sloped letters running all over a pile of notes in my father's bedroom.

Niamh had turned off her recorder, and we were both shrugging into our coats. I knew I'd turned puce. I could feel the heat on my face.

As we parted at the door, I shook her hand. 'Lovely to meet you, Niamh! Really hope to see you again'—which was another lie, since I had every intention of avoiding her like the plague.

Two minutes later I was in my car, tearing towards home.

•

The dogs greeted me as I pelted into the house. Dad was just as I'd left him an hour ago: under a blanket in the snug, fast asleep. I needed to be quick, and quiet.

I made a rapid search of his bedroom, then of the study, shining my phone torch into dark corners. No sign of the green box. I tiptoed through the front hallway, into the parlour with its window seat and Mum's neglected piano. Nobody came in here nowadays. If I wanted to hide something, this room might well be my choice.

It was a good call. The box had been jammed deep into the space between a bookcase and a wall, just visible in the glow of my torch. Dad's treasure. *HER*.

I smuggled it down to my own room and locked the door. I even drew the curtains, in case he happened to look in from the porch. I sat on the bed, drew a long breath and lifted the lid.

Eighteen messages in total, all of them written in the same forward-sloping hand as the Biddulph bivvy log. I ignored the four I'd already read, laying the rest on top of my duvet. Some were covered in square creases, as though they'd been folded many times. About half were written on sheets from the kind of notepad the drug company reps used to give doctors, with the company's logo along the top. Dad always had a stack of those advertising freebies—at work, in his house-call bag, by the kitchen phone.

I read each of them as they came out of the box. They referred to past conversations, to plans for the future, to happy moments spent together. Most were carefully vague: no names, no dates. Some arranged a rendezvous 'where we met the first time', or 'at the river'. Carrying on an affair took a bit of ingenuity, before the advent of mobile phones.

Among the last of the notes, I came across two more photos. There was Leah, hanging clothes on a line on the porch of an A-frame hut. It could be anywhere in the country, possibly several days' tramp from the nearest vehicle track. The picture was taken before the digital age, back in the days when we took films into chemist shops to be developed. Light had leaked into the camera, so that a ghostly flame consumed the slender figure.

The other photo, too, was scorched in the flame of over-exposure. The same hut, the same clothes on the line. The man in it looked athletic, swinging an axe high over one shoulder, ready to split the log that stood on a block in front of him. He was wearing a blue-checked shirt with the sleeves rolled up.

Nausea rose into my throat. That shirt! I chose it in a hiking shop in Auckland. I was a student, it cost more than I could afford, but I hoped he'd be pleased. Lightweight, useful in all weather, easy to dry. *Happy Birthday, Dad.*

I'd known my father all my life. I'd never known him at all.

With my gaze still fixed on the axe-wielding figure, I scraped the last two scraps of paper from the bottom of the box. I was reeling from the shock of seeing Dad, no longer quite so interested in the notes. I knew what to expect from them now: more geeky flirting, more serious-minded love, more assignations.

I was wrong. I was *so* wrong.

Felix! The time for argument has passed.

> *You stand to lose everything you've ever worked for. You'll be a pariah. People will despise you. They wouldn't spit on you if you were on fire. How would my mother feel about you, if she knew? Do you really want her to find out?*

> *At the very least you'll be struck off and never work as a doctor again. The consequences could be far worse even than that.*

> *Is this what you want? Disgrace and ruin? Exile?*

> *Of course not. That's why I know you'll do this my way.*
> *L*

And just like that, love had turned to menace.

The final note was scribbled on a blue post-it. The paper looked as though it had been rolled up tightly and folded in half, perhaps jammed into a small hiding place. The message was curt:

Good decision. Thank you. See you on Friday. L

I held my breath for a moment, as the implications sank in.

Such pitiless words. Such fury. She was blackmailing him. *Felix*—she used his name this time, perhaps because the affair was over and she didn't care so much about discovery. She was prepared to see him disgraced, ruined, drummed out of town, even out of the country. Maybe she had salacious details about his sexual preferences to reveal, just to add a bit of spice. What was she demanding in return for her silence? Money, or perhaps some kind of horrible humiliation?

Whatever the threat, he'd capitulated—or pretended to. She clearly believed he was ready to comply with her demands. She was smug. *Good decision. See you on Friday.*

She walked into the petrol station, banging on about those bloody snails, buying chocolate, being all chummy with me. How *could* she? What a cool operator. She was on her way to meet my father, to collect whatever it was she'd extorted out of him.

She drove up to the Ruahines, never to be seen again.

On a Friday.

•

I didn't know what to do. Didn't know what to do, or think, or hope for. I had no more sand in which to bury my head. My body took over—a violent clenching of my stomach, cold sweat on my face. I rushed to the bathroom, downed a glass of water and immediately brought it up again.

Then I sat on the floor by the toilet with my eyes closed, trying not to panic.

Fact: Dad had an affair with Leah. He was never what he pretended to be.

Fact: She was blackmailing him.

Fact: She said she'd see him on Friday.

Fact: She disappeared on a Friday.

Fact: He has confessed to being her killer.

Fact: I found a turquoise beanie in this house, identical to the one she was wearing when she set out.

Logical conclusion: My father is a murderer.

One plus one equals two.

My first instinct was to tell someone. Not Mum. Not Nathan—this was too much, too serious. Sarah often worked late at night. Perhaps I could send her a text, see if she was still awake? I crouched on the freezing bathroom floor, writing and deleting anguished messages.

But in the end, I knew I couldn't risk it. People talk. Even Sarah might not be able to resist telling someone, and the consequences could be appalling. I had to carry this burden alone. I had to decide what to do with it.

How did the law react when someone had committed an atrocity in the past, but was now sick and demented? I thought of war criminals, toppled oppressors who claimed they were too frail to stand trial. You saw them on the news: shrunken old men, handcuffed in the dock. Most people would say they'd earned their fate, that guilt doesn't diminish with time, that their victims cried out for justice. I'd rarely felt sorry for them.

That could be Dad: led to a police car and taken away. He'd be bewildered. He might die alone in a cell. That would be traditional justice, but what would it achieve?

I found I'd somehow got myself back to my studio, turned on the radio and picked up a pencil. There was nothing to do but keep going. I *must* keep going, or I'd collapse.

The disc jockey was playing nonstop music from the 1980s. You'd think that would be cheering, but no. Every song seemed to add a new layer of weirdness. Queen sang the praises of a crazy little thing called love; Cutting Crew had just died in someone's arms, that night.

Taking a sheet of translucent paper, I laid it over a full-size rough drawing and began to trace the outline of George, the ginger fluff ball. My hands were steady, but my mind was in a blender: chattering, screaming, whirring.

What about Raewyn and Ira? They'd never stopped waiting, hoping, searching, grieving. I had to tell them what I'd found. I *must* tell them. I owed them the truth.

But this truth was ugly. Leah blackmailed him; he murdered her. He hid her body and pretended to search frantically, day after day, ensuring that she'd never be found. He offered comfort and shed tears, all with her blood on his hands. He kept up his good-doctor-and-friend act for a quarter of a century. All these years, he'd been lying. Would they really want this kind of truth?

Ira ran around outside Biddulph's bivvy calling for Leah— and then he thought he heard her answer him, crying out from the depths of a steep bluff. But Dad persuaded him it was only an echo. And now I was wondering about that echo.

Soft Cell were singing about tainted love. I swept my pencil over the Christmas kitten's twitching whiskers—and Leah used the last of her energy to scream for help, and Dad led Ira away.

George was overjoyed at being fed and warm. His eyes were bright, his tail stuck straight up like the jaunty flag on a golf cart. He was climbing curtains in a palace drawing room. Admiral Flufflebum tried to stop him running amok, because the Queen was about to entertain the French ambassador in this very room.

Leah's voice, Leah's presence, Leah's absence. She was a blackmailer. She was writing her notes, pouring out her inner life.

I love you. We love one another. Have you any idea of the rarity of that?

People will despise you. They wouldn't spit on you if you were on fire.

See you on Friday.

Here were Her Majesty's royal feet, strolling through the door in sensible court shoes. Her Majesty never hurried. Here were the twelve turned-out paws of her corgis. Here were the polished brogues of the butler, the high heels of the charming French ambassador.

Here was a pair of red-laced walking boots. Someone had followed the lone hiker into the wilderness. Hunters carried dead deer and pigs up and down the hills, slung over their shoulders. Leah would be far lighter than a stag.

But Dad saved lives. He worked day and night to alleviate suffering. He had almost inhuman self-control. *I wish I were a robot.* There was no way—*no way*—he would turn to violence. Impossible.

Ah, well, but is that true, Emily? Remember the rosebuds? The soft, lovely rosebuds that he nurtured with such tender care. He sliced off their heads and trampled them into the dirt.

George bounced along the mantelpiece, pushing things off with a delicately curled paw. A thousand-year-old Chinese vase began to topple! *Oh no, George!* The French ambassador was once a gymnast. She was diving through the air, her arms outstretched. She was—

A shout—a crash, a thud—had me sprinting down to the snug. I found Dad face down on the floor among the pages of his newspaper, with the side table tipped over on top of him. Gyp scooted out from the chaos, tail between his legs.

'Dad!' I gasped. 'Are you all right? Did you trip over the dog?'

He was moaning, 'Oh dear, oh dear,' swinging his head from side to side. I kneeled next to him and tried to work out whether he was badly hurt. There were no obvious signs of injury.

'C'mon,' I gasped. 'Lean on me. Let's get you up.'

He thanked me. With a tremendous grunt of effort, he laid a hand on the sofa, and another on my shoulder. Together we pushed and pulled and somehow got him into the armchair. By the time he was sitting down we were both out of breath.

'You okay?' I asked, once his breathing had slowed. 'Dad? Should I get help?'

His gaze roved from my ear, to my mouth, to my eyes. 'I'm sorry. Who are you?'

'Emily.'

'Who?'

'Emily. Don't you know me, Dad? Your daughter.'

He peered at me wonderingly, like a toddler.

'And who am I?' he asked, with a small, hopeful smile; the kind of smile that teeters on terror.

His hair was a thatch, swept to one side by his fall. My immaculate father. It made him look crazy. I wanted to smooth it down for him, to make him dignified again.

'You seem a nice person,' he persisted. 'Please, could you tell me who I am?'

'You're Dr Felix Kirkland.'

He silently repeated the name, and then shook his head.

I reached for his hand, to save him from falling into the abyss.

'You are Felix Kirkland. You are my dad, who I love.'

His hand was limp, like a dead bird. I felt his mortality. My father, the colossus, reduced to this.

In that moment I made my decision. No matter what had happened between him and Leah, no matter what crime he had committed, he wasn't that person anymore. I wasn't going to let anyone take him away and ask him questions. I wasn't going to let him be one of those frightened old men in the dock. He was already lost. I would keep his secrets.

I became an accomplice.

TWENTY-SIX

Those were strange days, as the winter solstice approached.

The television news crew spent a whole morning at Raewyn's home. Their documentary was scheduled to air on the seventeenth of June; the newspaper planned to print the story on the same day. Leah's anniversary: twenty-five years since she walked out of her home for the last time.

Raewyn was nervous before the TV people arrived. She even bought a new jersey for the occasion.

'They were good at their jobs, though,' she told me later. 'Very friendly, very professional. It was strange to talk about Leah with cameras pointing at me, but I got through it.'

Dad and I kept one another company through the watches of the long nights. We made our camp in the snug, the metal chimney of the stove tick-tick-ticking as it expanded and contracted. I held his hand when he cried; I shushed him when he tried to talk about Leah, both of which happened more and more often. We pretended to play chess, we puzzled over crosswords; we drank hot chocolate with a liberal dash of whisky.

He generally settled down just as the sun was rising. I used to grab a jacket from the boot room and step out into the garden for a few minutes of calm. One morning I fell asleep in the pergola and woke up frozen. I forgot how it felt not to be tired.

But I hadn't lost him entirely. Not yet. Felix Kirkland was still in there. One evening over dinner he spotted me rubbing my aching neck, and briskly asked what the problem was.

'It's been giving me a bit of grief,' I complained.

'Want me to take a look?'

'Sure.'

He was already on his feet, coming around to my side of the table. He methodically manipulated my head and neck in every direction. He asked exactly where it hurt and how long this had been going on. He asked if I had spasms, or headaches, and what did I do for a living? Then he washed his hands at the sink, palms, backs, between the fingers, wrists, while reassuring me that I didn't need to worry.

'I think this is likely to do with your working posture,' he declared, drying his hands on a paper towel. 'You're an . . .'

'Artist.'

'That's right. And this has come on since you stopped working in your usual studio.'

'It has!' I cried, delighted. 'Dad—you're right! It has! Ever since I stopped using my adjustable desk and an easel.'

He nodded. Suggested I could use analgesics in the short term, but he suspected painkillers weren't the answer here. He recommended I have a critical look at the ergonomics of my work environment.

'Mention it again in a couple of weeks,' he said, 'if it hasn't resolved at all.'

It was wonderful to glimpse the man he'd been. I tried to hold on to the memory, because I never knew whether it would be the last time.

●

One frozen Friday afternoon, I nipped into the health centre to pick up a prescription for Raewyn. Pamela stopped to talk to me.

'How's your dad?' she asked. 'I was planning to drive out to your place to see him.'

I thanked her. I longed for her help, but I didn't dare to accept it. 'Maybe another time,' I said. 'He's not coping well with visitors just now.'

She regarded me shrewdly. 'He deteriorating?'

You know how it is: when you're frightened and sleep-deprived, and someone offers you a kind word, you dissolve into soggy mush.

'Maybe you could do with a bit of help?' Pamela suggested, laying her hand on my arm. 'We can refer him to the day centre at St Patrick's. Mind you, he might be a nuisance! He'll keep trying to examine patients.'

I thanked her again, but I turned down that offer too. 'He'd hate it,' I said. That was perfectly true, but it wasn't the reason why I couldn't let him out of my sight.

'It's not just his memory,' I explained, 'it's . . . him. His soul. Physically he's fit as a buck rabbit, better shape than I am. We have the most dug-over garden in Tawanui! He's not about to, um . . .'

'Not about to peg out?'

I was fiddling with the tag on Dad's car keys. 'He's in limbo. He's scared.'

'One day soon,' she said, as we walked towards the entrance doors, 'he'll slip behind the veil for good. He'll let go of what he's lost, which will be sad for you but much easier for him. He knew he was in trouble long before anyone else did. When I heard he was refusing medication, I wasn't surprised. I thought, *No, of course Felix Kirkland would make that choice, not to prolong things*. He always knew what he wanted, and he knew what he didn't. Once he made up his mind to do something, he'd see it through. He wouldn't let anything stand in his way.'

We stepped outside, making our way down the icy wheelchair ramp.

'Snow down to five hundred metres in the forecast for next week,' said Pamela, pulling her cardigan across her chest. 'My electric blanket is my best friend.'

The world felt watchful, the air opaque. Sounds carried with eerie, thudding clarity: the laughter of children in the playground, a clang as someone dropped scaffolding in a building site across the street. The Ruahines had been painted with a wet sponge onto a chalky sky. We were on a stage set: tiny people in a mouse-sized town, cowering beneath giant mountains. Snow had fallen again in the night, icing sprinkled down to the bush line.

'I gather half the town's going to be on the TV on Monday,' said Pamela.

'Mm. And in the papers.'

'Opening wounds.' She twisted her mouth. 'What's the point? We'll never know what really happened to Leah Parata. Personally, I've always had my suspicions about the hunters who claimed they were on Biddulph Road. Suppose one of them shot her by mistake? Happens all the time: people don't check their targets. They panicked, hid her body and made up a story.'

Her theory gave me a faint gleam of hope. Hunting tragedies were in the news every year. The disorientating effect of the bush, coupled with adrenaline, seemed to be a lethal combination. Someone would be absolutely certain it was a deer they were seeing through their scope, moving through the dense undergrowth—only to find they'd killed their brother or son or best friend.

'But the police spoke to those men,' I said doubtfully. 'Surely one of them would have broken ranks?'

'Depends how good they were at lying, doesn't it?'

I longed for this to be the truth. A tragic mistake, a cruel cover-up. But not a murder. Not Dad.

As I drove home, I kept replaying something Pamela said about him. She'd worked at the surgery for decades; she knew him in his prime.

Once he made up his mind to do something, he'd see it through. He wouldn't let anything stand in his way.

When it came to a blackmailing ex-lover, I was very much afraid she was right.

TWENTY-SEVEN

I woke with an aching sadness in my chest. It was 17 June. Leah's day.

The ranges were a battalion of white-boned skeletons. Biddulph's bivvy would be deep in snow. Silent, muffled. Perhaps the weight of it would finally bring down the roof and bury the whole place. Perhaps, at last, we could all forget.

I phoned Raewyn and was relieved to discover that Ira was with her, ostensibly fixing a problem with her shower. Good old Ira. He wouldn't let his mum go through this terrible day alone.

'We're both a bit jumpy,' said Raewyn. 'Not sure how it will feel, Leah being in the papers and on the telly.'

I was determined to get to the local newspaper before Dad did. One photo of Leah drove him into a frenzy; what effect might an entire article have?

I wrote a note to leave beside his armchair: *I HAVE GONE FOR A WALK. BACK SOON. EMILY.*

As I slid it onto the side table, he blinked up at me. Nowadays, the lights seemed to flicker on and off in his brain.

'Just taking the dogs for a quick run,' I said.

'Should I come?'

'No, no. It looks nice and sunny out there, but it's freezing! Snow way down the ranges. You stay warm.'

The Courier was waiting in its age-old place on the gravel at the top of the drive. The delivery guy hurled rolled-up newspapers out of his car window as he drove along, and somehow contrived to land it in that precise spot every time. Genius. I snatched it up without breaking my stride, headed straight for the school bus shelter and spread it out on the seat.

Niamh's feature was a four-page spread: THE TOWN THAT HAS NEVER FORGOTTEN. It led with the photo of Leah in the feathered cloak, with a blue academic hood, collecting her PhD. On the facing page, Raewyn was a solitary figure among her fruit trees, her back to the camera, looking towards the snow-capped Ruahines. The photographer had managed to capture the stoicism of her straight-backed posture, while making the mountains seem to tower over her.

She'd given a long interview, describing the work Leah was doing, the honours she'd won, all those golden hopes for her future.

'It was as though the bush had swallowed her up. We couldn't bury her next to her dad, who loved her so much. We never brought her home to say goodbye.'

The search coordinator, Dave Perry, told his side of the story. I'd known him as a fairly young man, but the photo in the paper showed a rugged greybeard in wet-weather tramping gear.

For Perry, and many others who searched during those weeks, the mystery is unfinished business. 'It's been a feature of my life,' he confides. 'The one person I never found, alive or dead. Every summer I hike along the route Leah took, hoping to spot something we missed. I once found an abandoned tent and hoped it was a clue, but it turned out to be unconnected to Leah.'

There was a photo of Biddulph's bivvy, one of Leah's hand-written log, two more of Leah herself. A map showed the region, with arrows and circles pointing out the relevant places. It confirmed what everyone already knew: there was nothing much out there except wave after wave of loneliness.

The write-up of my interview was a relief. Niamh had faith-fully reported what I told her in Forty Degrees that day, except she'd made me sound much nobler and kinder than I am.

Emily Kirkland, a neighbour of the Parata family who grew up with Leah, was perhaps the last person ever to see the missing woman. Leah stopped at the Tawanui petrol station on her way to the trail head, buying chocolate which she intended to take on her three-night hike.

'It's haunted us all,' Emily told me. Visibly distressed, she describes that final conversation. The pair discussed the poor weather, but Leah laughed it off. The rain, she said, would make the snails easier to find.

'Leah was no rookie. She was well-equipped, experi-enced, super-fit. She'd checked the forecast. She knew the country, she knew her bushcraft.'

Kirkland has spent the past twenty-five years living overseas, and is an internationally successful illustrator of children's books. Yet she, like so many in this close-knit town, is deeply aware of the long shadow cast by Leah's disappearance.

'She was Dr Parata,' she says. 'Everyone looked up to her.'

The article didn't speculate about bruises, violent boyfriends or a pregnancy. This was no hatchet job: Niamh had played it straight, not milked the story for every ounce of salacious rumour. She set out the findings of the police report, bolstering their conclusion with statistics about how many people vanished in New Zealand's beautiful, treacherous backcountry.

> Unexplained disappearances are startlingly common. On average, in recent decades, at least one person has vanished each year. Search and rescue volunteers have a grim name for this cohort of The Disappeared. They call them 'Beam Me Up, Scotties', because it seems as though they have been teleported from the face of the Earth.

There you are then, I told myself later, as I shoved the newspaper into the stove and watched it burn. *Happens all the time! Just another statistic. Nothing to see here, folks.*

•

That evening I was pottering around the kitchen, making a tuna bake—one of the few meals Dad could still taste. He was watching a program about the midwinter arrival in the skies of Matariki—the Pleiades cluster—which marked the Māori New Year and was celebrated with a country-wide festival. Dad had pulled his armchair very close to the television, his face three feet from the screen. That was normal for him nowadays. Perhaps he was struggling to make sense of the moving images.

As I slid the baking dish into the oven, my mind was on the Buckingham Palace horses. I'd spent an unproductive afternoon, wrestling with the layout of a tricky double-page spread. Perhaps I should have been concentrating on Dad, but I couldn't stay alert and twitchy for every second of every day. I didn't expect the story about Leah to come on any time soon; I thought we had at least another half-hour, until after the main news.

Gradually, her name filtered into my consciousness: *Leah Parata . . . Leah Parata . . .* and suddenly Raewyn's voice, as clear as though she was in the snug herself. Dad's fingers were clamped around the wooden arms of his chair. I leaned in the doorway, watching over his shoulder.

Raewyn sat at her kitchen table. A story-book grandmother: her hair in an old-lady bun, grey wisps down her cheeks. Her interviewer was a well-known journalist with a sympathetic touch.

'She was so clever,' said Raewyn, as he nodded encouragement. 'Not just academic. She'd her judo black belt, she rode, she played the bagpipes. She was a devastating debater, and the people she worked with at Victoria University said she was a wonderful teacher. Everything she did, she did well. Leah never panicked. She stayed calm in a crisis. Most of all, she was the best daughter any mother could ask for.'

'You lost your husband,' murmured the interviewer.

While Raewyn answered him, we were shown the photo of Manu's last Christmas day.

'His long illness was very, very difficult for all of us,' she whispered. 'Leah kept us going. She had that strength, that bloody-minded grit. When Manu finally died, we all thought we'd faced the worst life could throw at us. But . . .'

The film cut to Raewyn again. She'd broken off in mid-sentence. Those bastards! Why didn't they stop filming? The camera panned down to her hands, clasped together, fiddling with her wedding ring.

The journalist's voice was gentle. 'It was just a couple of years later that she disappeared, wasn't it?'

'It was two years and three months after we said goodbye to Manu.'

'And she hiked into the mountains that day because of a research project?'

'All about an aerial drop of 1080, and whether it could save the Marchant's snail. She was surveying for monitoring sites.

She would have been taking teams up there later on—she'd done it before.'

'And I think she stayed here with you, the night before?'

'Yes, she always did. In her bedroom—it was still her bedroom, though she'd left home. On the Friday morning we had a cup of tea together. I sat here, she sat just there. Then she washed up our mugs, left them on the draining board, said she'd better be off and would be back by Monday lunchtime. She picked up her pack— *See you, Mum!*—and she walked out through that door.' Raewyn pointed over the interviewer's head. 'Monday came, but she didn't. She never came back. You can't imagine how that feels. People tell me I should move off the farm, maybe into town. But how can I? Tomorrow might be the day she walks in through that same door. She'll be fifty-one now, but to me she's still a young woman.'

'Do you have a message for people who may be watching this?'

'Did anyone see her? Did anyone give her a lift? Please, if you did, come forward. Even if it's bad news. I'd rather know. No parent should have to live like this, without knowing.'

Another image filled the screen, one I'd not seen. Leah, looking very much as I remembered her in the petrol station that day: wearing a navy blue jacket, with the turquoise beanie in her right hand. She was stretching out her left arm, obviously pointing at something. I couldn't take my eyes off her. The high forehead, the mole on her cheek. Her intensity, her irrepressible confidence.

She was looking straight into the lens.

She was looking at me.

Dad hadn't moved a muscle since the interview began. He stared impassively, eyebrows raised, deep furrows in his forehead. I kept glancing at him, fearing what might be going on behind the blank immobility. Did he remember this woman as a lover? A blackmailer? A victim? Or maybe there was no recognition today, no lights on at all.

Raewyn's interview was followed by footage showing the spot where Leah's car was found. Then we heard from Dave Perry, who stood with folded arms as he described the weeks of searching. As he spoke, photos of teams combing the countryside appeared on the screen. I spotted a very young Todd Tillerson— and suddenly there was Dad, poring over a map, looking tired and serious.

The final words were given to Raewyn.

'Leah would have done something that mattered. She would have helped to save this planet. You just wonder . . . why? Why didn't she come home?'

And back to the studio, where the solemn-looking presenter recited a phone number for anyone with information to call. Seconds later, we were watching an advert for McDonald's.

Still no movement from Dad. His gaze was fixed upon the cavorting, Happy-Meal-scoffing children as intently as it had been upon Leah. He hadn't released his grip on the arms of his chair.

'Hey?' I whispered, touching his shoulder. 'Okay, Dad?'

Without a word, he reached his hand across to grasp mine. His didn't feel like a dead thing now. There was warmth and strength. I'd intended to console him, but the opposite was happening. It seemed as though he was reaching out to guide me, because I was lost. I wanted to take the moment and preserve it forever.

I felt the pressure of his fingers through all the adverts, through the final section of the news, through half the police procedural that followed. He'd never held my hand like this before, not even when I was a child.

When the next ad break began, he announced that he was going to fetch warmer clothes from his room.

'Chilly,' he said, letting go of my hand and pushing himself to his feet. 'Another southerly. More snow, I should think.'

I threw some of Ira's neatly split logs on the fire, and fetched our tuna bake from the oven. When Dad reappeared, he was wearing a thicker sweater. His steps had purpose.

'Smells as though there's something delicious cooking,' he said, rubbing his hands.

We ate supper on our knees in the snug, because it was so warm by the fire and perishing in the rest of the house. I'd turned off the TV, in case they ran some of those clips again.

'Now,' Dad began, with no preamble, 'you're not going to marry the lawyer, are you? Can't remember his name. Flies a plane.'

I was taking a sip of red wine at the time and snorted so violently that much of it shot up my nose. 'Todd? No!'

'He seems a decent-enough man. Good-looking, I'd have thought.'

'He's all of that. But . . . just no. I don't think either of us would think that's a good idea. He's . . .' I hesitated. 'I mean, quite apart from the fact that I wouldn't want to live in Tawanui forever, and I genuinely like being single, you do know he's gay?'

'Ah!' Dad looked relieved. 'If I knew, I'd forgotten. Good, because I think you should go home to . . . I hope you'll get on with your own life.'

'I absolutely will. But not yet,' I said firmly, and left it at that.

Later, he insisted on doing the washing-up. 'You cooked, least I can do.'

I'd just picked up a tea towel when Ira phoned.

'Did you see it?' he asked.

'We did. Raewyn was amazing. Are you still with her?'

It was subtle, but I could tell he'd been drinking: a slight dragging of his speech, seesawing in pitch.

'Yup. We watched it together. She's pretty upset now. So am I, to be honest. Seeing Leah on the screen—no warning—was a bit of a gut punch.'

'Are you okay?'

Stupid, empty question. Of course he wasn't okay.

'We've started on the whisky,' he said. 'Raising a glass to Leah and Dad.'

I heard Raewyn's voice in the background: 'Say hello from me.' Steam had misted on the windows. I used the tea towel to rub an oval hole, blinking at my reflection. Deep into the black mirror, Dad was standing with his hands in the sink, apparently lost in thought.

'They've already had calls to that hotline,' said Ira. 'But nothing new. No miracle.'

'It might take time.'

'There isn't going to be a miracle. She's gone. God knows where, but she's gone.'

After he'd rung off, I stood looking into the window. There was my face, my shapeless mop of hair; there was Dad at the sink, the dogs lolling by the glow of the stove through the archway. Dad made no comment about the fact that Ira had just phoned me. Perhaps he wasn't even aware of it.

Beyond our reflections, starlight gleamed on the snow-skeletons of the Ruahines. Freezing air seeped through the gaps around the door. Shivering, I drew the curtains.

As I turned back to Dad, he came to life—suddenly, as though a switch had been flicked.

'Almost finished,' he said. 'Just these'—he plonked a couple of foamy glasses upside down onto the draining board—'and this.'

He'd produced the sharp kitchen knife I'd used for chopping the onions. Light flashed on the blade as he brandished it. For a moment he looked sinister, like the villain in a film, creeping up on the girl in the shower.

'I think I'll say goodnight.' He was putting the knife away in the wrong drawer. 'One or two things I'd like to get done before I hit the hay.'

'Night, Dad. Sleep well. See you tomorrow.'

His hand was on the doorhandle when he hesitated, turned back, and smiled at me. Periwinkle eyes, Einstein-crazy hair.

'Don't worry,' he said. 'Everything's all right.'

•

It had been a long day, after another disturbed night. I could barely keep my eyes open. I tried sketching a birthday card for Mum, but after five minutes found I was falling asleep over my pad, and crawled off to bed.

Out like a light.

For the first time in weeks, Dad didn't wake me. Not even once. It was bliss.

TWENTY-EIGHT

Gloria padded into my room, yawning loudly. It was a polite way of telling me she was hungry.

A tui fluting and whistling in the garden; pale light behind the curtains. A whole night's sleep! I stretched, patting the dog's head. Even before I was out from under the duvet, I knew the temperature had dropped again. I could feel the damp clinging to the walls. Complaining to Gloria about how effing cold it was, I drew my curtains. In the glass-clear air of early morning, the ranges seemed to be marching ever closer to Arapito. The snow was a cascade of white, right over the foothills, even a thin shimmer of it across our lawn. Clouds hung in puffs as though flurries were being blown upwards.

Gloria and I headed along to the kitchen where I fed her and Gyp. I had an uncomfortable feeling, like a stone in my shoe. Dad was normally up by now, but I hadn't heard him.

I took a cup of tea down to his room. His curtains were closed, his wallet and phone on Bert's chest, his empty bed carefully made. I'd slept in, like a lazy lummox, but he was obviously having a good day.

A quick check reassured me that his orange hiking jacket was gone from the boot room, along with his walking boots. He'd dressed properly for the weather; he wasn't wandering around the farm in pyjamas and bare feet. He would be at Raewyn's, most likely. Bacon and coffee. I hoped he wasn't pouring out confessions about Leah, but I doubted it. He'd seemed sharp before he went to bed, and was always at his best in the morning.

I cleaned the kitchen, paid some bills, took a shower in the ice-cold bathroom. The stone in my shoe kept jabbing my heel, but I ignored it. I was enjoying the peace too much. That's the awful truth.

As I emerged from the bathroom, rubbing my hair with a towel, the grandmother clock struck the half-hour. Ten thirty. Gyp and Gloria trotted down the corridor to greet me, helicopter tails. That's when it occurred to me that it was odd, very odd, that Dad hadn't taken them with him on his outing.

Grabbing my phone from beside my bed, I called Raewyn.

'Felix?' She sounded anxious. 'I've not seen him.'

I stood in the silent house with my hair dripping between my shoulder blades. One moment, you can still pretend everything is okay. The next, you know it isn't.

'Has he taken his car?' she asked.

'No. I keep the key hidden.'

'Have you checked the well?'

She'd barely spoken the words before I was jumping down the porch steps, pelting into the blue-frost shadow beyond the carport. Drifts of frozen rose petals glistened around the edges of their beds; the lid of the well was encrusted with countless tiny crystals. So much beauty, so much fear. The lid was heavy, designed to deter small children and animals. I heaved it up, dragging it to one side. Then I crouched down on the edge, shining my phone's torch into the darkness.

No floating corpses. I could have cried with relief.

'He's not in the well,' I told Raewyn, who hadn't hung up.

She said Ira was with her now, and would begin searching the farm while she looked everywhere between our two houses. She also suggested I call the health centre.

'I know Felix has no transport,' she said, 'but he's more than capable of walking to town.'

None of his ex-colleagues had seen him today. Pamela came on the line, speaking in that fake-calm voice people use when they're secretly concerned.

'I'm just on my way out to home visits,' she said. 'I'll spread the word.'

'Thanks.'

'I bet he's having coffee with some old patient right now.'

'Hope so.'

The cat was out of the bag. Within half an hour, the whole town knew that Dr Kirkland was missing. Todd phoned to say he was taking his plane up for a bird's-eye search. Pamela rang back to tell me that people were checking in their sheds and outhouses, as though Dad was a lost cat. Anyone who came across him would bring him home.

They'll talk to him too, I thought. *And if he seems distressed, they'll ask him what's wrong.* I had to get to him first.

Raewyn set out in her car, checking all the roads between us and town. I saw Ira crisscrossing the farm on his quad bike. He stood up as he drove, looking down into the Arapito ravine. Cattle sometimes missed their footing and fell off those cliffs, often to their deaths. Why not people too?

Gloria and Gyp seemed to know something was wrong, their tails waving at half-speed as we checked the shelter belt, the woolshed, the bus shelter. I splashed knee-deep in the freezing currents of the river, dreading what I might find. Dripping, shivering, I clambered up the hill at the back of Ira's farm, shouting for my dad at the top of my voice. I hadn't yelled like this since

I was a child—loud and high and panicked. My shouts seemed puny, swallowed by the wind.

In a few hours' time, it would be dark.

•

'So you last saw him ... when?' asked the man who answered the police non-emergency number. I could almost hear his pen, hovering over a half-filled report. Tawanui police station was rarely manned these days. The guy I was talking to could be anywhere.

'Ten o'clock last night,' I told him. 'By this morning he was gone.'

The wind was getting up, looking for trouble. I imagined Dad huddled in a ditch, his teeth chattering. Perhaps he was trying to find his way home. Perhaps he didn't know what 'home' meant anymore.

'Sure he's not in the house?' asked the police officer. 'You'd be amazed how often people turn out to be fast asleep in a cupboard. You got a cellar? Attic? Check those places first. Under all the beds.'

'I've searched every inch of this house.'

'Car?'

'Still here.'

'Could he have used public transport?'

This guy *really* wasn't a local.

'There is no public transport in Tawanui. Hardly even a taxi. We're not on an InterCity bus route.'

He was maddeningly upbeat. 'Seventy-five-year-old with dementia, on foot. He's likely to be within a kilometre of his home. They generally are. Have you spoken to your neighbours?'

'I have,' I said. 'They're searching too.'

Someone would be round to my place, he assured me. It could be a while, though. Several officers were caught up in a serious incident in Hastings. In the meantime, they'd be asking patrol cars to keep an eye out for a man of Dad's description. Elderly, white hair, dark orange jacket.

'Nine times out of ten,' he said cheerfully, 'it's a false alarm. They pitch up, safe and sound.'

•

That day seems blurred, when I look back on it.

I had a message from Nathan, asking what date was Mum's birthday. He also asked how I was doing, and I couldn't lie. I told him his granddad was missing, that it would be dark by about five, and that I was expecting sub-zero temperatures overnight.

He replied within seconds, bless him. *Want me to book a flight to NZ?*

Definitely not! I answered, though at that moment I'd have given my right arm to teleport him into Dad's kitchen. *I've called the police. I want you to carry on with your adventures.*

I couldn't put it off any longer. I had to contact my siblings. Nathan was in touch with his Kiwi cousins, so the social media drums would soon be beating. Eddie and Rhonda were on holiday in Fiji, and to my intense relief he didn't answer his phone; Carmen reacted exactly as I'd known she would.

'You haven't seen him since *when*? For God's sake, Emily! Do I need to get myself down there?'

She spoke to someone else, her voice muffled, as if she had one hand over the phone. 'My dad . . . yes, he has Alzheimer's. I can't drop everything. Well, actually we don't know he's okay, do we?'

'The entire town's out looking for him,' I assured her. 'I've called the police. You can't help. Stay put.'

'I *knew* this was going to happen,' she moaned. 'Why, oh why, wouldn't he go into St Patrick's?'

•

They seemed all wrong for the kitchen, somehow, with their heavy shoes, their bulky stab-proof vests and radios: a silent young man, not much older than Nathan, and a calm woman, perhaps in her thirties, who introduced herself as Sergeant Jodie Palmer.

'So you've checked with friends and neighbours?' she asked.

'Everyone.'

She glanced into the pantry, as though expecting to spot a retired doctor perched among the tins. She had a very straight fringe, hair scraped into a ponytail.

'Does he often go out on his own?'

'He often walks his dogs, or goes to visit our neighbour. I've never lost him before.'

'Did he have access to cash? Credit cards? Could he have decided to take a little holiday, maybe staying in a hotel or with a friend?'

'No. I mean yes, it's theoretically possible, but it's just not what he'd do.'

At her suggestion, I went online to check his bank accounts. He'd spent nothing in weeks. All the outgoing transactions were mine, shopping or paying bills. He might have a bit of cash, but that would be all.

She asked about the most obvious dangers: gullies, wells, hazardous bodies of water. There's something ominous about that expression, *body of water*. I had a sickening image of Dad, face down in the swirling eddies of the river, old-man's hair floating like a halo of pale waterweed.

'My neighbour has searched his farm, including the dams,' I said. 'I've already looked in the nearest parts of the Arapito stream, and the well in our garden.'

Jodie had obviously received training on how to talk to the families of lost elderly relatives.

'Sometimes, when a person who's confused wanders off, they've been talking about a place they used to live or work. Maybe his childhood home? Office? A wife's grave, that kind of thing? The advice we give is to start by checking those places.'

'He's from Leeds, in England. Mum's alive and well, but long divorced from him. He was a doctor at the Tawanui Health Centre, and that was his second home for forty years, but they've not seen him at all today.'

She looked thoughtful, peering out of the window at the gathering dusk.

'D'you think he might have tried to walk there? Long way on foot.'

'About thirteen kilometres,' I said. 'We thought of that. My neighbour—Raewyn—has been driving around all afternoon, but she's had no luck. He's still fit, the distance probably wouldn't be a problem, but the dementia might be.'

'Okay.' Jodie took a swift glance at her watch, chewing her lower lip. 'We'll head out that way too.'

I saw them to their car. Jodie said she'd start pulling levers to bring in LandSAR, the land-based search and rescue volunteers. As she opened her door, she paused. 'You've checked the garden shed, obviously?'

'About five times.'

'Can you think of anything—anything at all—that he's been mentioning or obsessing about? A while ago, we ran a major search for a lady with dementia. Turned out she'd managed to board an InterCity bus to Auckland! She was going to see her mother. She'd been talking about it: *I'm going to see Mum. I'll take the bus.* But her mum had been dead forty years.'

'That's really sad,' I said. 'Poor lady.'

'Mm. What about your dad? Sure there wasn't anything like that on his mind?'

Leah. Leah was on his mind.

I tried to look mystified and baffled, holding out my hands to show that I had nothing. 'He's been his normal self,' I said.

I watched their tail-lights on the drive; saw Jodie turn right and begin to crawl along Arapito Road.

A wife's grave, that kind of thing. Start by checking those places.

How about the scene of a murder?

•

I was beginning to regret my decision to try to navigate Biddulph Road alone, late at night, in a car that wasn't designed for off-road adventures. The unsealed track was littered with potholes, slips and fallen branches. Trees and undergrowth reached out from both sides, clawing at the aerial, scratching the doors. I was heading right to the edge of the map, and beyond were dragons. No light, no dwellings, no phone signal. Break down, run off the road, I'd be on my own.

My headlights made ghost-tunnels through the pitch-dark, teeming with a trillion insects, as the track began to wind steeply uphill. On and on, creeping around hairpin bends, ready to brake if Dad suddenly stepped out in front of me. Wooden bridges rattled. I stopped on each, wound down my windows and shone my flashlight into swollen streams gushing down rocky gullies. My imagination was in overdrive. I had a ghastly sensation that someone was sitting in the back seat behind me. I kept checking over my shoulder.

The call had gone out on social media and radio news that evening: *Have you seen Felix Kirkland?* They used a photo I took with my phone: Dad, standing among his roses. Jodie Palmer had been in touch to let me know they'd checked with bus and taxi companies and drawn a blank. The local volunteers were on board, and a coordinated search was to begin first thing tomorrow morning.

Raewyn had offered to wait in our house in case Dad re-appeared. Ira was driving around farms and lifestyle blocks, asking people to look in their outbuildings. He and I had agreed to meet up at the petrol station later.

Biddulph Road ended in nothingness. I cut the engine, then my headlights. Silence. Even the wind was holding its breath. As my eyes began to adjust, I opened my door and climbed out. I had a vivid image of Leah doing the same thing, in this same place. A bar of chocolate in her pocket, turquoise beanie on her head.

See you on Friday.

Perhaps he was waiting for her here. Perhaps she was strangled—or bludgeoned, or knifed, or shot—right where I was standing.

No . . . no. That didn't work. She wrote her log the following morning. Saturday. She was definitely in the bivvy then, alive and well. Perhaps they'd spent the night together. He might have ambushed her somewhere up there—easy to hide a body, and almost no chance of any forensic evidence being discovered. Did she know what was coming, in the end? Did she beg, did she fight for her life?

'Dad?' I whispered.

Darkness crouched over me, pressing its thumbs into my eyes. I swear the hair really did stand up on the back of my neck. I flicked on my flashlight, directing its beam in a long arc into the deepest shadows. Nothing but trees. Millions and millions of trees, all of them watching me.

'Dad?' I croaked again. 'You here?'

The silence exploded with the rasping growl of a possum—guttural, seething, almost on top of me. My wildly swinging light picked out two pairs of glowing eyes in the foliage above my head. I can't remember when I've moved so fast. I was back in the car, spinning the wheel in my desperation to turn around, mud flying as I sped away down the track.

•

Ira laughed when he heard how a pair of small creatures put me to rout.

'Creepy, aren't they?' he said. 'They look cute, but they sound like devils.'

It was getting on for midnight. The petrol station was closed. Still, its dimly lit forecourt felt positively jolly compared to the menacing void at the far end of Biddulph Road. I shone my torch into the drive-through carwash while Ira nipped around the side of the building to check the outdoor toilet.

'Dripping tap,' he said, walking back. 'The floor's a lake. No Doc Kirkland. He's probably bedded down in some nice warm barn.'

'You should go home and get some sleep,' I told him.

'So should you.'

But neither of us made any move to leave. We leaned on the cooling bonnet of Dad's car, under the blue light of the fuel price sign, and tried to think of new places to search. Eventually we lapsed into exhausted silence, listening to the wistful cries of a morepork. She sounded very close, perhaps hunting in the trees alongside the road.

'How's it going with the hot vet?' I asked.

'Terrifying, actually.' Ira hesitated before adding, 'She is planning on moving in with me.'

I swung around to peer at his blue-lit face. 'That's so great! But you and her, and two little boys, all in your tiny shack?'

'She wants to move a house onto the site where mine is now. She reckons it's a world-beating location.'

'You never tell me anything!' I pretended to punch him on the arm. 'How can I not have known this? When are you going to tell Raewyn? When do I get to meet Cathy?'

'Steady on.'

I shut up and let him do the talking. 'It's early days,' he said. 'Don't want to get Mum's hopes up if it isn't going to happen.'

But they'd already found a house to relocate; they'd even got a quote for hauling it onto the site and connecting it up to plumbing and electricity. This was astonishing, wonderful news—a hope-coloured splash of light in the sea of darkness.

'I decided not to do that test,' said Ira. 'For the Huntington's gene.'

'What made you change your mind?'

'I had a long talk with the genetic counsellor. She helped me to think really clearly about why I'd be taking it, and how I'd react if I got a positive result. I've got to be honest with myself—I don't think I'd handle it very well at all. I won't have kids of my own, so there's no chance of passing it on. And we're all going to die one day, aren't we? Leah got tested and she was free of Huntington's, but her card was still marked.'

'True,' I murmured, thinking about Dad and Leah, wishing I could tell Ira everything I'd discovered.

'Every human being has a use-by date,' Ira was saying. 'Cathy understands that reality. Sean might not make very old bones, because he has Down's syndrome. And her husband was just biking home from work when a truck took him out.'

'That's terrible.'

'It is. But first, there's life! The clinic people said I'm showing no red flags at all. No early signs. I'm older than any of my relatives when they first noticed symptoms. So it's looking hopeful. I'm just going to assume I'd test negative. I'm going to take my chances, and get on and . . . well. Live. Just live.'

I couldn't resist hugging him. Suddenly I felt swamped by joy for my friend, by fear for Dad. I was burbling all kinds of tearful nonsense about how lucky Cathy was, and how I hoped she damned well knew it or she'd have me to answer to.

'C'mon,' said Ira, awkwardly patting my arm. 'We'd better grab a couple of hours' sleep, if we can.'

I was getting into my car when the morepork began to call again. The little owl could see by starlight; she would be able to hear every sound, even the rustle of her insect prey in the leaf litter beneath the trees. The night was her world. I wondered whether she knew where Dad was now.

Perhaps Ira was having similar thoughts. He stood still, his head tilted, listening to the owl.

'We'll find him tomorrow,' he said. 'We'll bring him home.'

TWENTY-NINE

The first searchers began driving up to our place at dawn.

They were a team of volunteers from LandSAR, led by Dave Perry. Jodie Palmer arrived at almost the same time, having changed her shifts to see this search get underway. Everyone spread out maps on the table, looking anxiously at weather forecasts on their phones and asking me how far Dad might have travelled on foot. Another southerly front was approaching. Gales and snow to low levels were due tonight.

Over the next hour, we were joined by a steady stream of locals: ex-patients of every demographic, tramping club members, medical colleagues, staff from Kauri hospice. Long lines of searchers were soon walking across the land surrounding the house. The plan was to comb a five-hundred-metre radius at first, then wider, looking for any clue—a dropped wrapper, a footprint, anything.

Dave Perry gave everyone a role. Raewyn took over the kitchen, dishing out hot soup and drinks. Ira was dispatched with a group down the Arapito stream. I fielded calls and acted as general guide. Todd was up in his Cessna, working his methodical way around a search grid.

My siblings both phoned. Carmen was trying to hire a locum, but it could take several days. Eddie and Rhonda were still in Fiji. If Dad didn't turn up soon, they'd try to get a flight back. Neither could resist *I-told-you-so*. If only he were safely in St Patrick's right now, they said. If *only*. This wouldn't be happening.

The social media appeal had already yielded calls to the police line. The most hopeful was a sighting of someone very like Dr Kirkland in the town of Waipukurau, boarding an Inter-City bus to Wellington. The passenger inventory was checked, the driver questioned, visits made. The Felix Kirkland look-alike turned out to be a man in his sixties, heading south to visit a woman he'd met on Tinder.

'Long way to go for a blind date,' said Jodie. 'I hope it was worth it.'

My role for the afternoon was to walk towards town, checking every possible hiding place yet again. I'd reached the road gate when a white Ford Ranger swept past me and parked. The driver might be about forty. Freckles, jeans, gumboots. A riotous mass of frizzy hair, shoulder length. I knew exactly who she was.

'Cathy,' I said, hurrying towards her.

'Hi.' She sounded uncertain, glancing at the dogs trotting around my feet. Perhaps she was better at remembering animals than she was their owners.

When I introduced myself, she smiled. 'Admiral Flufflebum! My boys are fans.'

She explained that she'd come to help in the search, and was there any news? On a normal day I'd have invited her home for coffee and pulled out every stop to get the lowdown on the woman who'd managed to melt Ira's heart. Not today.

'No news,' I said. 'Ira's been out checking the river.'

When I told her where I was headed she suggested she come along too, and we take one verge each. She rummaged through a stack of equipment in the back of her truck, emerging with a flashlight and a waterproof jacket.

We made our way down the muddy gravel of Arapito Road, checking every ditch, every stand of trees, every creek. We shone our lights down culverts, in case Dad had crawled into one and got himself stuck headfirst. I remembered what he said about people with hypothermia, how they sometimes try to burrow. It was a horrifying thought.

'Thanks for coming along,' I said to Cathy.

'Least I can do. You must be beside yourself.'

'You're not working?'

'I've had two call-outs early this morning, got the rest of the day off. My children are at school. Their grandparents are going to pick them up.'

'Sean and Alex.'

I heard her chuckle. 'Their fame goes before them.'

I noticed how she stopped and waited for me whenever I was checking the depths of a concrete drain or under a clump of bushes. I think she wanted to be on hand, in case I stumbled upon Dad's body. I was grateful. I liked this woman. Both dogs did too, which I thought was a good sign. She kept calling to them and rubbing their ears.

As we talked, she volunteered the information that she and Ira might move in together.

'But I haven't even met his mother!' she said. 'I'm not sure she knows of my existence.'

'She does. She's guessed. You'll love Raewyn.'

'That's what everyone tells me. But the family member I'm really worried about isn't his mother. It's—'

She broke off, as Todd passed low overhead. I had no idea who she might mean. Ira's only close relative was Raewyn. There was extended family on Manu's side, but they would never interfere in Ira's life.

'Who are you worried about?' I asked, once we could hear one another again.

'His sister. Leah. Her name seems to be taboo—and with Ira, it's what he *doesn't* say that matters, isn't it? I have this feeling he's thinking about her whenever we sit out on his porch, on those awful old chairs, and look up at the mountains.'

Another culvert. I dropped down into the ditch and lay on my front, shining my torch down the soaking tunnel. I was trying to calculate whether it might be large enough for a human being to squeeze himself into.

'Someone's coming,' said Cathy.

I heard a vehicle rumbling up the track, slowing down, stopping. A car door slammed. Hoping it might be the police with good news, I scrambled to my feet. But instead of Jodie Palmer in her uniform, I found myself facing the long, thin figure of Vince Price. He stood with his hands in his pockets, rocking backwards and forwards on steel-toed boots. A black beanie covered his monk's tonsure. I groaned silently. I wasn't in the mood for fantasies.

'Hi, Vince,' I said, switching off my torch. 'Come to help with the search?'

'I have, actually!'

Instantly, I was ashamed. I'd made assumptions about a man's mental health.

'Thanks! Well, if you go on up to our house, Dave Perry's there. He'll tell you what to do.'

'You can call off the search. It's a waste of time.'

'It is?'

'They've been in touch. They want you to know that Dr Kirkland's gone to the same place as Leah Parata.' He tipped his head back, smiling peacefully as though he could see all the way through the vault of the sky, right into heaven. 'He's loving it. They say you're not to worry at all.'

His words brought me closer to tears than all the sympathetic nods and pats-on-the-arm people had showered on me that morning. Vince had such unshakeable conviction. It was wonderful, in its way. He truly believed what he said, and he meant to comfort me.

'Thank you, Vince,' I said, saluting him with my torch. 'That's good to know.'

From her side of the road, Cathy watched him turn his van around in a gateway. He gave us both a friendly wave as he passed again. Message delivered.

'Be nice if he was right,' she said. 'I'd like to think aliens were kindly people.'

We searched for another two hours. MetService had been right about the weather packing up: fading daylight brought plummeting temperatures and rising winds. Our torch beams seemed more and more feeble, and we still had to walk back. Cathy needed to collect her sons soon.

As we turned around, she stopped. She stood in the road, frowning as she peered towards the blurred outlines of the ranges, disappearing beneath a granite cloud of blizzard. I knew what she was thinking.

'He wouldn't have headed up there, would he?' she said.

•

Dad's kitchen was full of people rubbing the circulation back into their cheeks and talking about the weather. Nobody said it out loud, but all of us were thinking it: nobody could survive prolonged exposure to these conditions. Unless Dad was under cover, he'd be dead by morning.

'Let's hope there's a guardian angel out there,' murmured Raewyn.

Several thoughtful souls asked if I wanted them to stay, and was I all right in the house alone? I assured them I'd be fine. One by one they got into their cars and left, though many would be back tomorrow. Raewyn stayed long enough to watch the regional news, which featured footage of the search. We saw Jodie Palmer give a short press statement, admitting to 'grave concerns' for the safety of Dr Felix Kirkland. They still hoped he was indoors, perhaps in a hotel or staying with a friend. There was a number to call.

I told Raewyn about Cathy. It was a bit of good news for her, at least.

'The woman in the white ute,' she said. 'I knew it! Is she going to break his heart?'

'I don't think so. I like her very much.'

'Any other day,' sighed Raewyn, as she pulled on her coat, 'I'd be clapping my hands and shouting, "Hallelujah!" Today it doesn't seem to matter. Not while Felix is lost.'

She'd just slid the kitchen door open when a violent gust of wind seemed to punch the whole house. It sounded disturbingly like a human scream.

'Oh, Felix,' she moaned, shivering as she looked out into the storm. 'Felix, Felix, you silly man. Where are you?'

•

I couldn't think of indulging in the luxury of a warm bed, knowing Dad was out there.

I wandered around, drinking coffee and looking in cupboards yet again. I climbed right up into the attic. Then I remembered Gyp, and the rats, and had the awful idea that Dad might somehow have got himself trapped *under* the house. I spent the next half-hour with a torch, commando-crawling among the rat droppings and bumping my head every time I lifted it too high. The storm raged above me. There were animal bones in that revolting place, and the desiccated corpses of birds, and great blankets of cobwebs with living spiders that ran down my neck, and nameless lumps of . . . *ugh*, I didn't even want to think about it. The whole experience was grim. But at least there were no dead fathers under there.

Standing in the dismal shower, I shut my eyes and felt the trickle of hot water run over my eyelids. I was trying to recall every detail of our last evening together. He took my hand as we sat watching the TV. He got a thicker sweater, ate his tuna bake, did the washing-up. He was cheerful, wasn't he? Almost elated. Odd, really, when we'd just sat through that painful documentary. We talked about Todd Tillerson. Dad told me to go home, to get on with my life. That was odd too, now I thought about it.

The bathroom felt like a walk-in fridge. Even the towels were damp. I galloped straight from the shower to the snug, threw logs into the stove, dressed and wrapped Dad's soft blanket around me. It smelled of wood smoke. It smelled of Dad. *Where are you?* I kept imagining his footsteps on the porch. Twice I ran to the kitchen door and threw it open, hoping to see him standing there, perhaps stooping to take off his boots as he'd done a thousand times before. Both times I stepped outside, listening and shouting into the wind and dark.

Eventually I stretched out on the sofa. Just for a minute. Not to sleep, just to rest. Dad must be freezing. *Hypothermia. Of all the ways to go, it's not the worst one.*

I woke with that heart-thumping sense of doom that always follows a nightmare. Or a death.

On his way to bed, he'd turned back from the door and smiled at me. Right at me. He looked happy. Periwinkle eyes, Einstein-crazy hair. It was one of those loving moments, when he seemed like the father I'd always wanted. He turned back to tell me something.

Don't worry. Everything's all right.

Don't worry. Everything's all right.

Don't worry . . .

I was awake. Violently awake. And I knew what to do.

•

This was no time for finesse. I dragged my case from under the bed, scattering summer clothes, my passport and other detritus across the floor. There it was. Manila, A4-sized, curling at its edges. *NOT TO BE OPENED UNTIL AFTER MY DEATH.*

Back in the snug, with Dad's blanket draped over my shoulders, I slid my finger under the flap, ripped off the masking tape and drew the contents of the envelope into the thin yellow light of the standard lamp.

On top of a pile of pages lay a single sheet of cream writing paper, covered in Dad's post-dementia handwriting. Blue-black ink smudged here and there, childishly large letters with wobbles in the lines. Several words had been scribbled out. I imagined him gripping his fountain pen, fighting to keep the thoughts in his mind long enough to get them down.

It was a letter. It was addressed to me.

Arapito
January 2019

My most beloved Emily,

I've had the enclosed document ready for some time, but now that I know you are coming to see me, I will give it into your sensible hands. You have my permission to read it—please do read it. I composed it over some months, on those days when my memory was clear. I began to write everything down when I realised that I was profoundly compromised. I felt I must record all of this before I forget it. If and when I forget, the truth will be deleted from history. What happened will be deleted. What I did.

I presume that you've paid heed to the instructions on the envelope, and opened it only after my death. What you do with this document, and the information it contains, is up to you. I have written it in the form of a letter to

Raewyn Parata, with the intention that it be shown to her. I should like her to have it, but I cannot know whether that will be the right thing to do when the moment comes. I leave that decision in your safekeeping.

I'm sorry to land you with an awful responsibility, but only you can gauge the situation at the time. In any event, I no longer trust my intellect to make such cataclysmic decisions.

I have always believed that TRUTH is to be guarded and cherished. When it's eroded or twisted or obscured, human life disintegrates. We see that in the world's politics, we see it in our own families. Yet I myself have abused, eroded and obscured the truth. I've peddled unforgiveable lies. As you will see when you read, I have committed the deadliest of sins and compounded it with interest, year on year.

I don't ask for forgiveness, nor do I expect it. I am profoundly ashamed. Yet I think I would do it all over again if I had to.

I love all three of my children, and all my grandchildren, though I may not understand them well. But I have chosen to trust you with this truth, because you, I think, are the most likely to listen to my voice. I hope you'll know what to do with it.

Your ever-loving
Dad

I could almost hear him speaking. I *could* hear his voice.

The document he mentioned was a sheaf of A4 paper, closely typed, held together with a bulldog clip. The sheets felt slightly soft and damp, probably as a result of their long sojourn under my bed. Crouched on the sofa, with my legs tucked under me, I began to read.

And it turns out the truth doesn't always set you free. Sometimes it destroys you.

•

I stumbled up the track towards Raewyn's house. The Pleiades cluster was rising. Matariki. A dusty glimmer, hanging above the horizon—the midwinter herald of dawn. Perhaps Dad was watching it too.

I'd just spent the darkest hours of my life sitting on the sofa with a blanket over my shoulders. I couldn't take it in, couldn't believe this thing that had happened. The earth had shifted on its axis. The pain, the ruined lives.

Twice I determined to destroy everything: the contents of Dad's envelope, the photos and notes in that green box. I gritted my teeth, grabbed it all—muttering *right!*—and threw open the door of the stove. Embers glowed and winked up at me, ready to leap into flames and consume the unbearable. One flick of my wrist—*poof!* Gone! Out of sight, out of mind. Wouldn't that be the right thing to do? Wouldn't everyone be happier, in the long run?

Twice, I shut the door again. I couldn't bring myself to burn the truth.

I'd reached Raewyn's road gate. I could see a distant glimmer of light in the house—of course she was up before dawn, worrying about Dad. I stopped in my tracks.

'No,' I groaned aloud. 'No, no. I can't.'

A magpie called from the telephone wires—gently, as though it was singing a lullaby, not pecking a child's face. I was spinning on the ball of my foot in the gravel, around and around, tapping the envelope against my cheek—*What do I do? What the hell do I do?*—and then I was running away, back towards Dad's house. I didn't have the courage. I would burn the lot. End of story.

But I have chosen to trust you with this truth . . . I hope you'll know what to do with it.

'You're wrong, Dad!' I wailed. 'I haven't a bloody clue what to do with this fucking truth of yours.'

I stopped again. Turned back again. Retraced my steps. And this time, I kept going. I was about to lob a grenade into my friends' lives.

Before I'd reached the top of the ramp, I saw a flurry of movement and the kitchen door was thrown open. Raewyn was wearing a jersey over a floor-length nightdress, her hair loose. Ira stood behind her with a mug in his hand, no doubt getting ready to begin yet another day's searching.

'Is he back?' Raewyn gasped.

I shook my head.

'Tell me what's happened,' she said, drawing me inside. 'Tell me! I can see there's something terrible. I can see in your . . . Is he dead?'

'I think so,' I said.

Without taking her eyes off my face, she sank into a chair at the end of her kitchen table.

I hesitated for one last moment before sliding the envelope across to her.

'For you,' I said. 'From him.'

THIRTY

Arapito
July 2016

My dear Raewyn,

I do not know whether this letter will ever be finished, nor whether you will ever read it. What I do know is that I must begin to write it now. My mind nowadays is much like my television screen: blurry, flickering. Eventually, it will go blank for the final time. When that happens I shall be erased. More importantly, the true story of your life, and mine, will be erased.

Today, I stood in Hawke's Bay airport and watched Emily and Nathan get onto a plane. They stood at the top of the steps, smiling and waving in my direction. They couldn't see me through the window, but I was waving back to them. I don't know whether I shall ever see them again. I watched them disappear inside the aircraft, and I felt the wasted opportunity of their time with me here. I felt so very small.

Then came a very frightening thing. I went out to the airport car park, but I had no idea where I'd left my car.

I looked, and looked, and tried to remember, but I had no memory at all of parking the car. The parking-car moment had fallen into a chasm, a treacherous drop-off with no light or time. I thought of looking for cars of a similar colour, and then I experienced a moment of terror—not just fear, not just disquiet: screaming terror. Because I could not remember anything at all about my car!

Just as I thought all was lost, the mist cleared. Hurrah! Of course, it's a dark blue Toyota, parked on the left, waiting for me in all its glorious familiarity. You can imagine my relief. But that moment was a warning shot across my bow. I'm losing the battle. Time is short. Now is the moment to write this letter.

First, the confession: I've been lying to you for over two decades. I've allowed you to believe that Leah died a lonely but natural death, and even to hope that she's still alive somewhere. I've lied because she asked me to, but also to protect myself. I think this may be one of the factors that has driven me to dementia. I deserve it.

Where to begin?

Begin with Leah, of course. Leah is at the heart of everything, isn't she? Her presence had such weight, such brilliance, that everything else seemed to revolve around it.

She would have been about eleven when we first arrived in Tawanui. Your children and mine all ran around your place and ours, they piled on and off your school bus. I remember a strong, dauntless girl riding across the farm, up and down those steep gullies, mustering sheep with her father. Even then she was fearless. Just a child, of course—and I didn't see her as anything else. That is not my sin.

But time passed. Your family endured the years of Manu's illness. Leah left home and began her academic career; my unhappy marriage came to an end when Lillian returned to England. One day, visiting Manu, I was surprised to find a poised adult competently looking after her father. Leah was writing up her PhD thesis but had come home during the long summer break, knowing he was nearing the end.

Leah was, of course, extraordinary. Her intellect, her energy, her constant enquiry—these set her apart. She thought with absolute rationality and independence of mind, along with that wry humour which made me laugh more than I ever had (not a high bar, my children might declare; they think me dour). She shared my fascination with the natural world. And so, despite the wide disparity in our ages, we became friends during those final months of Manu's life. Close friends. But her father was my patient, she was the same age as my own children. At this time, I assure you, we were no more than friends.

Leah began post-doctoral research on the impact of pest control. We wrote, we phoned, we talked, and talked, and talked. I have never felt such a connection with another human being. Indeed, until that time I hadn't believed such a thing was possible.

One weekend, she invited me to accompany her on a research trip into the Tararua Range. That was when we became more than friends. You'll think I took advantage of her. You'll think me grubby, ridiculous, obsessed, going through a midlife crisis. She was in her mid-twenties, I in my late forties. She was still registered as a patient at the Tawanui Health Centre, though she swiftly moved to a GP in Wellington.

I was in love with Leah; how could I not be? She was the love of my life. That's a cliché. It is also, in this case, the simple truth.

We weren't ashamed, but we knew that our being together would cause trouble. Leah was afraid I'd be ruined. My involvement with a young woman I'd known from her childhood, who'd been my patient, might destroy both our reputations. We were also very afraid of hurting you, Ira or my own children.

For over a year, we kept our secret. If I had a meeting or conference at the hospital in Palmerston North, Leah would travel up from Wellington to meet me. Sometimes she drove to the western side of the ranges while I set out from here. We'd each walk in and meet in one of the remote huts, or we'd camp. Leah's research on the *Powelliphanta marchanti* was wonderful for us, because it brought her home to Tawanui. That was the happiest time of my life.

There were no mobile phones, no texts, the world was not yet in the thrall of email. Leah's landline was in the kitchen of her shared flat, and she worked in a room with other postgrads. So we wrote real letters and posted them, or left notes for one another. Her favourite note-leaving spot was in our school bus shelter. There's a nook at one end of the seat, where we jammed much-folded letters. It served us well when Leah was home: dry, hidden and inconspicuous for either of us to nip in there. Her idea, of course. She was far better at the subterfuge than I. She enjoyed it, whereas I really did not.

We made two wonderful trips to the South Island. I drove my car onto the Cook Strait ferry while Leah jumped on as a foot passenger and met me, smiling, in the lounge. We've camped on Stewart Island, listening to the shrill of a kiwi. We've stayed in a bach in the Nelson Lakes, reading books, watching films and behaving like any other happy couple. Sometimes I worried that she should be looking for a man her own age, who could be a father to her children. When I mentioned this, she was scathing. Age, she said, was an artificial construct and irrelevant to her—and anyway, she would never have children. She was at risk of developing Huntington's disease and might pass it on to the next generation. I know that Ira feels the same. It was only during this time, 1993, that the hereditary version of the gene responsible for Huntington's was identified and a reliable test developed. Leah told me about it; she kept up with all scientific developments. But these were very early days, and the test wasn't yet available in New Zealand.

One afternoon, when tramping in the Ruahines, we made an orienteering mistake. We battled our way along a spur for hours, only to realise that we weren't at all where we'd thought. We were also running out of daylight. We blundered about until, dropping into a gully, we found ourselves in a magical Eden: a clear stream, a small waterfall, a sheltered spot to bivvy for the night, and some of the richest flora and fauna either of us had ever seen. The little valley rang with birdsong. In the evening we heard and saw long-tailed bats.

In the months that followed, we often returned to our private Eden. It's far from any trail, but we navigated a route via Whio stream, starting halfway along Biddulph Road. It's entirely possible that no human foot has ever—to this day—trod in our gully, except for ours. *No human foot*. Think of that, Raewyn. Think of that.

But our joy involved an awful lot of deception, and we wanted the secrecy to end. We planned to tell you. We talked about marriage. Leah felt it would legitimise things, help to quell the inevitable small-town gossip and judgement. She said she'd make an honest man out of me! We decided to keep our secret just a few months longer, until after Carmen and Richard's wedding. It would have been unforgivably selfish to spoil their day with our scandal.

Leah also had another secret, one which she hoped would come to nothing. She hid it from me as long as she could.

I weep when I think of those golden days, planning our future, looking forward to a lifetime together. One of my happiest memories is bathed in the heavenly light of a summer sunrise. We'd spent the night by our unnamed stream, and Leah was cooling her feet below the waterfall. I took a photo of her there—I have it still. I was singing aloud. I felt alive!

I remember saying that I'd never been so happy. I was brought up to feel unworthy of happiness, and I was afraid that some terrible hammer must be about to fall. Leah came splashing to kiss me. She declared that no bloody hammer would dare to fall on her! And I believed her. Leah's buoyancy kept me afloat.

But later that same morning, as we were hiking down the steep stream bed, she fell heavily. Sharp stones caused contusions on her knees and hands. She cursed herself for not looking where she was going, laughed off my offer of first aid and set off faster than ever—leaping from rock to rock. She was like a mountain goat. I had to work hard to keep up.

I didn't see her again for almost a month. She said she was snowed under: preparing for the new academic year, tackling research grant applications and rewriting her thesis for publication. I was busy with the long-planned extension to the surgery so couldn't get down to Wellington. Perhaps that's why I dropped the ball. I noticed a change in her tone when she phoned, a flatness, but put it down to overwork.

But when she next came home, I knew that something was very wrong. The energy and optimism had drained out of her. She arranged to meet me by the bridge where Biddulph Road crosses Whio stream. I was sure she was going to end our relationship, and I wouldn't have blamed her for one second.

I'll never forget it. We sat in her car, watching a pair of twittering riflemen in the branches of a kowhai. They were arguing, hopping from one twig to another. Leah called them lucky guys, because they didn't know whether a predator was creeping up on them. They just lived each moment.

Then, ever so casually, she mentioned that she had 'a little bit of a worry'.

A little bit of a worry.

Those six words marked the boundary between heaven and hell.

A little bit of a worry.

I stopped breathing. I felt as though my heart had stopped, too. I saw Manu, sitting in his tidy town clothes in my consulting room.

A little bit of a worry.

Leah told me that there was something she'd been keeping from me. She had been noticing unusual things about herself for years, perhaps as many as five years—she couldn't be sure how long—but they had come on so gradually that she'd been able to minimise and deny, blaming hormonal changes or the pressures of life. She had to work harder and harder to stay at the top of her game academically, but persuaded herself that this was inevitable because the challenges were ever greater. Recently, though, these problems had become impossible to ignore. Her typing had become clumsy; she kept striking the wrong keys.

She bumped into things. She dropped things. Most distressing was a loss of mental acuity. 'I just can't seem to concentrate anymore,' she said. 'The other day, I forgot my own phone number! I feel hopeless, as though I'm going mad, I'm always on edge.' She described storming into a senior lecturer's office and ranting at him about the timetable. 'Fred was shocked. I *never* behave like that!'

As I listened, my own hands began to shake violently. I gripped them between my knees so that she wouldn't see my terror. I tried to reassure her. All this could be easily reversible, I said. It might be a virus—had she ever had glandular fever? Could be a thyroid problem, an infection, a vitamin deficiency. Might even be depression. 'I'll arrange for you to have some blood tests,' I told her. 'We'll get to the bottom of it. Don't worry. Don't worry. Please don't worry. We are in this together. I will never leave your side.'

When I ran out of reassuring words, she took my shaking hand and held it to her lips.

And then I began to remember things—small things, which I'd stubbornly refused to see. A change in her gait. Movements in her fingers, which I'd shrugged off as fidgeting. An elegant, but odd, circling of her wrist before she used her hand. Bursts of irritation.

Leah knew as much as anyone about the diagnosis and prognosis for Huntington's. She was young to be showing the symptoms. She hadn't expected them to appear, if at all, until middle age. But sometimes it does strike the young—and there's evidence that it tends to progress faster when it does. This is the final proof, if any were needed, that God is an utter, vicious bastard. Or non-existent. Take your pick. Perhaps he is both.

We met later at the surgery, after hours. She wouldn't see her own doctor in Wellington. She didn't want mention of Huntington's on any official health records. I took blood to send to the lab, for what I told them was a routine check, and did a series of basic neurological tests. What I found was so sinister that I was physically sick later on. Her reflexes, fine motor skills, balance and short-term memory showed subtle abnormalities that would ring alarm bells in any patient. And in her toes, the first stirring of the chorea—the involuntary jerks and twists, the St Vitus' dance which might take over her whole body as the disease progressed. She didn't even know her feet were twitching. I didn't mention it.

I would have given my life for this not to be happening. I would have died for Leah, without a second's hesitation. I had to tell her what she already knew: that her clinical presentation, together with her family history, put Huntington's high on the list of possible diagnoses. But, I said—*but*—it was only one possibility. The blood tests might show other conditions, the symptoms might resolve spontaneously. We shouldn't despair.

She, of course, had lived with this risk since childhood. Sitting on the edge of my examination couch, legs swinging, she said she wouldn't take the genetic test even if we could arrange it, because it would later be traceable back to her. She wouldn't see a specialist. There was to be no paper trail whatsoever. Could I do that? If the blood tests indicated that her symptoms had a more benign cause, well, wonderful.

'But I know what this is,' she said. 'I can feel it. I *know*. And I'm not going the way Dad did.'

That was the start of months of waiting and observing. Months of terror. The blood tests showed nothing reassuring, but still I kept hoping, hoping, hoping for her symptoms to disappear. She carried on with her working life, concealing her problems by sheer force of personality. A stumble and fall down a flight of steps left her covered in bruises, so she invented a collision with a mythical young man. She rarely visited you, Raewyn, because you were the person most likely to recognise the signs. She even announced that she'd somehow managed to have the genetic test, and that it was negative. I couldn't approve of this lie, but she was implacable: *I will not put my mother and brother through it again!*

And then, late one night, I had a terrible phone call. It was the only time I ever heard her panic. She didn't sound like herself at all. She said her mind had seized, statistics meant nothing to her, she couldn't process information. She was stricken. 'I'm losing control, I'm dissolving. It's happening too fast.'

I know how that feels, now that I'm in much the same boat. I understand at last.

I drove straight down to Wellington and arrived in the early hours. Her housemates were away. She'd already lost weight, dark circles around her eyes, her hair unwashed and unkempt. I'd brought medication to take the edge off her anxiety and help her sleep. I persuaded her to lie down, made her warm. I felt as though my heart was being torn out of my body.

That was when she first asked me to help her to die.

She'd been thinking about this for years, she said, and had decided that it would be best if she were simply to disappear. She could live without her strength, even without her dignity, but not without her intellect. Her aim was to die in the place she loved, while protecting me from the slightest possibility of suspicion. She'd already formulated a detailed plan. Leah had overcome one obstacle after another to become a leader in her field, and now one faulty gene was destroying her. *I'm not going to let this bastard of a disease win! I'm going to cheat it!* Having a clear plan gave her some kind of control over her destiny.

When she outlined it to me, including the part I was to play, I refused point blank. I was horrified.

She simply shrugged. Okay, never mind. She'd manage without me. She felt hanging herself might be the best option, or possibly drowning. She was wondering about the Cook Strait ferry. She lay there, considering the pros and cons of her options as though she were choosing a fabric for some new curtains.

Please believe me, Raewyn, when I promise you that I argued that day, and again, and again. I reminded her that a person can live for decades with Huntington's, that there was constant research and soon there might be a breakthrough—a cure, or at least an effective treatment. There were clinical trials going on, perhaps she could apply to join one? She was ready for my arguments. She'd kept a close eye on research around the world; she knew it was hopeless in her timeframe. She believed the next generation might have hope, but it was too late for her.

I talked about the terrible pain her plan would cause you and Ira. I urged her to let me tell you what was going on. She forbade it. Her logic was that you'd spent over a decade nursing Manu, and you could not do it again.

'Raewyn won't have to,' I said. 'Because *I* will. I want to.'

I imagined an unbearable future without her. I imagined your future, too, and Ira's, and the insupportable grief that you were soon to face, whatever decision she made. I racked my brains to think of a way to save her.

I had to leave her flat in the morning, because Lillian was due to arrive for Carmen's wedding. Leah walked out onto the street with me, and we agreed to talk again after the wedding was over. I didn't want to get into my car. I held on to her, begging her to stay alive.

I think about my behaviour, now that I too am facing neurological decay, and I wonder how I could have been so selfish.

She wrote to me later that same day. I've kept her letter. I'll transcribe some of it here. I want you to see that she really meant it.

You think my plan is heartless. You think I should 'let nature take its course'.

Felix, put yourself in my shoes. Since I was twelve years old, I've known I was at risk. I've known this since the day you came to our house and broke the news to my parents. That's why I've been driven. I feel my mortality. Every day of health and strength is priceless. Dad used to say to me, 'Ehara i te ti—you only live once, don't waste it.' He, of all people, knew how true that was.

You and I both know what's waiting for me. We both watched Dad become skin and bone, a puppet on strings, forced to dance and dance and dance. We both saw him regress into a second infancy. I didn't want him to leave us, but I wanted his suffering to end. If I could have given him something to make him fall asleep and never wake up, I would have.

Huntington's destroys people, it destroys families. You saw Mum taking care of him day after day, year after year. It almost broke her. And you want her to start all over again? No! Enough is enough.

I'm not afraid of dying (okay, I am! We all are, aren't we?) but I'm afraid of becoming that puppet. When I was sixteen, I made myself a solemn promise. Whatever

happened, I WOULD NEVER become that puppet!
I WOULD stay in control. I would choose the time and
manner of my leaving. I was going to call the shots.

This decision changed my life. Once it was made, I
could stop being afraid and get on with living. And I did.
I got on with it.

But now the time has come, and I'm going to keep my
promise to myself, with or without your help.

Raewyn, how do you imagine I felt when I read this letter?
What right had I to deny her the escape she'd promised
herself? Besides, I had no doubt that she'd go ahead on her
own, if I refused.

I went to meet Lillian at the airport. She thought I was
still angry about the divorce. 'What's eating you?' she kept
asking. 'You're even less fun than usual!' But she soon
gave up on me, in all the excitement of the wedding plans.

My daughter was getting married. That should have
been a day of joy, but it was the opposite. My horror
nearly caused me to collapse in the car, on the way to the
church. As the organ played and we walked up the aisle,
I saw Leah sitting between you and Ira. She was serene,
with painted-on colour in her cheeks and wearing a long-
sleeved dress that helped to conceal her painful thinness.
She smiled at me, gave me a thumbs-up! How did she do
that? Her courage was relentless.

I gave Carmen away. I made a speech, as you know.
I was on autopilot. I felt a lead weight pressing on my chest.
Towards the end of the evening, Leah and I danced. It was
a slow dance and normally we wouldn't have risked it, but
that night we felt as though we'd nothing left to lose. She
looked beautiful but the strain was showing, despite her
careful make-up. Keeping up the act had exhausted her.

As we danced, she said people—including you, Raewyn—were already commenting on her weight loss. Soon you'd notice other things. She had refined her plan, and wanted to carry it out within days.

I replied that even if I did help her, I'd be handing myself in afterwards. I could not, *would* not, leave you and Ira in ignorance.

She wasn't having it! My getting struck off the medical register with a criminal conviction, quite possibly a jail sentence—and public enemy number one—how would that help her family? She'd rather take a leap off the ferry.

At the end of the song, Eddie cut in. He was very drunk, perhaps you remember? He took her away from me, and the next moment he was all over her. I could have punched him. Leah told me later that he suggested she come back to his room to 'carry on the party'. She could handle him, but she left without speaking to me again.

The next morning, I found she'd left a note in the school bus shelter. She'd be grateful for my help, but she wasn't going to let me throw everything away.

You'll be a pariah. People will despise you. They wouldn't spit on you if you were on fire. How would my mother feel about you, if she knew? Do you really want her to find out?

At the very least you'll be struck off and never work as a doctor again. The consequences could be far worse even than that.

Is this what you want? Disgrace and ruin? Exile?

Of course not. That's why I know you'll do this my way.

We met by Whio stream. We sat in the winter sun, clutching at one another even as we argued bitterly. What a waste of our priceless time together! The last grains of sand were falling through the glass.

I tried, yet again, to persuade her to live on. It was all words, words. She was exasperated by my feeble backtracking. She didn't want to hear about my bloody principles! How dare I talk to her about dying with dignity? It was she who was looking down this barrel. 'It's not happening again,' she said. 'Mum and Ira aren't living through that nightmare. I'm not having them feeding me, wiping my bum, talking to me in baby language.'

I remember the rushing of the stream, clear water running past our feet, and yet we were in hell. I could taste acidic grief burning my throat while Leah used logic to coax and persuade me. Step by step by step.

'I'll come with you,' I told her. 'We'll go together.'

She wasn't having that, either.

'We aren't Romeo and Juliet. You're not a teenager. You can live without me—and you must. Don't you dare use me as an excuse to give up on your life.'

I implored her not to leave me. I promised I would stay beside her through every moment of the years ahead, that together we'd make them good years. I argued that her life was still priceless.

She pressed her fingers against my mouth. 'Stop,' she said. 'Please stop. If I've ever meant anything to you, please don't argue anymore.'

Raewyn, that is when I gave in to your courageous daughter. I couldn't possibly have had her sectioned, even if I'd been prepared to try—which I was not. If anyone on the planet was capable of making this decision, it was Leah. Had I refused to help, she would certainly have gone ahead regardless. I don't think she was driven to it by depression; she was driven by logic. She knew exactly what she was doing. She'd have died alone, by some awful means—or been left alive but with a ruined liver, a broken body or damaged brain.

I agreed to do it her way, and to keep her final secret. Was I wrong?

Was I?

I've asked myself that question every day, in all the years since.

Was I wrong?

I followed Leah's plan to the letter.

As soon she was sure I understood all the details, she drove back to Wellington. She wanted to leave her data and method easily accessible, ready for whoever took over her research. She worked without a break from that Sunday until the Thursday, when she made her final journey home to Tawanui.

Meanwhile, I was able to get hold of what she'd requested without any trouble. Back in those days there was far less regulation and red tape, and my work for the hospice meant that I constantly handled drugs used in palliative care. Nowadays it might be impossible; back then, nobody questioned me. Nobody even noticed. I wished they would.

The day came. The dreaded day. The day I have never forgotten, even when the names of my own children have slid from my mind.

On that Friday, I pretended I was driving down to a medical conference in Palmerston North. I set off early in the morning, dressed in a jacket and tie. There was indeed a medical conference, but I didn't attend. I hid my car well off the track on Biddulph Road, changed out of the conference clothes and set off, running up to Biddulph's bivvy. I saw nobody on the way. Leah had checked the forecast and picked days likely to have the worst possible weather for hiking in the Ruahines. First, she reasoned that we were in less danger of being spotted; second, it would more readily be assumed that she'd met with an accident. 'They'll say I took risks. They'll say I was too gung-ho, I made a fatal mistake. That's good.'

I spent only a few seconds in the bivvy. I was there just long enough to remove the original hut notebook and replace it with Leah's log—the very same one that Ira and I 'found'. Then I walked out, stuffing the real hut book into my pocket. I later burned it.

Leah wrote her false log the day before, at your kitchen table. I was with her. I watched her tear a page out of her own research notebook. I watched her write in the false time and date: *7.30 am, Saturday 18/6/94.* Her coordination and fine motor skills were giving her trouble, but she managed to make her handwriting look unremarkable. She dropped her pen several times, picked it up and carried on. Two words were spelled wrong, easy ones which she would have spelled correctly at the age of six. I forget what they were. She was angry with herself, crossed them out before deliberately laying her mug across them, obscuring her mistakes with a ring of coffee.

Those notes were Leah's final words to the world. And they were all a lie. She wasn't going across the saddle or along the ridge. She never went anywhere near Biddulph's bivvy. She would never complete her survey. Her beloved Marchant's snails must manage by themselves from now on, without their vigilant friend.

While I was sprinting back down with the notebook in my pocket, she was having that last cup of tea with you, Raewyn. Saying goodbye to you, she told me, was the only moment when her resolve faltered. She used every last resource in her body, determined to behave as though this was just a routine hike. She picked up her pack and walked out to her car. You cheerfully waved her off. When I picture that moment, my guilt chokes me.

I later learned that she pulled in at the petrol station to buy chocolate. This was her idea too, formed on the spur of the moment as she drove past. She wanted a witness who could confirm that her intention, as she drove towards the trail head, was a three-night hike. She deliberately discussed her fictional route with Emily. She deliberately sounded over-confident about the weather. Emily could confirm that she was alone in her car, with no other vehicle nearby. Leah wanted no gossip about the existence of a companion on her hike.

You see? She'd thought of everything.

She was waiting for me, as arranged, at Whio stream. She'd prepared exactly as she would for a long hike: food, a primus, camping gear. I was in a state of sickened misery. She seemed bright and alert, in better spirits than she had been in weeks. I asked her how she could laugh, and she replied, 'Because I'm cheating this bastard disease of all its fun!'

The walk took us over six hours, far longer than usual. I carried Leah's pack. We scrambled along the secret route we'd come to know well: following Whio stream for two hours or so, then up a steep ridge until we joined a spur. Our own stream—which I think has no name—has its headwaters in one of those valleys to the south. All the streams were in flood; we had to crisscross them continually, which was gruelling. Low cloud came billowing to meet us, the trees dripped, we were soaked. Normally I'd have revelled in being with Leah in our private world, but not that day. Each step took us closer to the end of the journey.

Every so often Leah would stop to look under decomposing logs, sorting through the leaf litter, the damp ferns and lichen. When her search was rewarded with the discovery of a live Marchant's snail, she seemed overcome with delight.

'*Powelliphanta marchanti!* Look, Felix. Isn't he majestic? Look at the beauty in that shell. He could be twenty years old.'

She was still living every second to the full, you see. Every second of her life. She fell often, once sprawling full-length after tripping on a vine. Her elbow was bleeding, her gloves were soaked through, but she didn't want pity. Not her. She ate some of the chocolate she'd bought from Emily, then grabbed my hand, crying, *Onwards and upwards!*

What drove her on, hour after hour, was her own indomitable spirit. She had made a promise to her sixteen-year-old self, and nothing was going to stand in her way. She was one of a kind, Raewyn. I shall never know her like again.

She was exhausted by the time we reached our little valley. The rain had stopped. I helped her into dry clothes, with thick socks for her cold feet. We sat beside the stream, below the waterfall. I leaned my back against the bank with my arms around her, and she rested against me. This was where she'd stood on that glorious morning, when she said no blow would ever fall on us.

'Are you thinking about the last time we were here?' she asked.

I said I was, and she nodded.

'Remember me like that,' she said. 'Remember me well and happy.'

As evening came on, the cloud lifted to allow us a glimpse of clear sky. Moss and algae, the whirr and whistle and fluting of birds. Long-tailed bats zipped up and down the stream, too fast for thought. When a morepork began to call, Leah's mind turned to her father.

'He told us the morepork was Hine-ruru,' she said. 'The owl woman, a guardian spirit who watches over the night. She guides people.'

I lit her primus stove and made coffee, sweet coffee to warm her. It was all I could do. I had no magic wand. I had no deity to call upon. I had only small, physical comforts. If love had any power—if my life could have saved her—I would have laid it down with absolute joy. She used her coffee to chase down the two antiemetic medications I'd brought, which were to be taken an hour before the lethal dose. When I saw her calmly take them, I broke down and sobbed like a child. She wiped my eyes. I still remember the feeling of her hand on my face. The aliveness.

I brought out mutton sandwiches, as she'd requested. She'd chosen them because they reminded her of family trips to Porangahau beach, when you produced endless mutton sandwiches and bottled peaches and biscuit tins full of baking. Neither of us touched this last meal.

In that last hour, Leah talked about her childhood. She said she had the best family in the world. She told me how you worked half the night to darn her jerseys and socks, how you'd never let her go to school without her hair plaited. She talked about Manu, and those wonderful camping expeditions with him and Ira. He would tell them stories once they were all in their sleeping bags at night. She described lying on a bed of ferns, listening to her father's voice, looking up at the stars and thinking that this was happiness. The Ruahine Range was her home.

I begged her one last time. *Please stay. Please don't go. Please don't leave all of us who love you so much.* But I'd seen her struggle that day. I'd seen her dropping her pen, spilling her coffee. Sometimes she lost her train of thought halfway through a sentence. She would break off and stare at me, as though the word she'd forgotten might be written on my forehead. She knew all of this was just the beginning. She knew where it would end.

She'd chosen a place just above the stream. It was hidden by undergrowth, sheltered by a magnificent silver tree fern. I flattened an area, unrolled her sleeping bag inside a waterproof bivvy bag, made a pillow from some of her clothes. I worked very, very slowly. I didn't want the task to end. I wanted to freeze time—to be in that place, with her, forever. I look back, and I wonder how I was able to do it at all. I don't think I could now.

Leah was taking me through her plan again. 'So, Felix. Listen . . .' She wanted to be sure I was going to follow it to the letter, when she was no longer with me. Can you imagine her voice?

'You must, *must*, get going as soon as it's light enough to walk out. Just go. Don't mess about! Promise? Leave me as I lie. If I'm ever found, it has to look as though I was lost and hypothermia got me. There must be no clues that I never intended to return. Don't take anything of mine away, okay? Except the cup with the traces of barbiturate, that might be a bit of a giveaway. And for God's sake, don't leave anything of yours as incriminating evidence!'

When I protested that I couldn't just abandon her, unburied and unmarked, that it was barbaric, she climbed up from the stream.

'Please,' she said, taking my face between her hands and touching her forehead to mine. 'Please do this. Yes,

yes, I know about the pigs and the rats and the flies and the maggots and everything else. Why would I care? You're a doctor, you know about the process of decomposition. Buried, unburied, what's the difference? My body will end up being recycled one way or another. I want you to leave me right here, in my home, under the open sky. Let me become a part of this place.'

She made me repeat my promise not to confess. Not to anyone. Not ever. I wasn't to be a bloody idiot (her words: *Don't go being a bloody idiot, Felix*). 'They'll come straight up here and get me,' she said. 'I'll be carried down in a body bag, and cut up in an autopsy. I don't want to end up buried in Tawanui cemetery, while you're in prison.'

Then she looked at her watch and said, 'Well, it's been an hour.'

I brought out the powdered pentobarbital I'd brought and stirred it into water in her cup. If I was going to help her do this, I was going to do it properly. Leah said this was the first time in her life that she'd actively encouraged a man to spike her drink. I said that wasn't funny. She said, 'Of course it's funny, Felix, don't be such a stuffed shirt.' At that, I began to cry again. She was ten times the human being I am.

I couldn't bring myself to give her the cup, so she reached out and grabbed it from my hands.

'I hope this stuff works,' she said, laying it on the ground beside her as she got into her sleeping bag. 'I'm going to be very pissed off if I go through all this, only to wake up again in an hour.'

I still thought we had more time. I still hoped I could stop her.

She said she felt a bit chilly. She asked me to fetch her merino cap from by the stream where we'd been sitting.

So I did—I dropped down the bank to grab it for her. I only turned my back for a moment. Just one moment. But it was enough. When I looked again, she was draining the cup. She grimaced, muttered 'bitter' and ate the last of the chocolate, which she'd bought for precisely that purpose.

I ran back to her in a panic, screaming, *No! Leah, no!* I was thinking about how to make her bring the poison back up, despite the antiemetic.

'It's okay,' she said, holding open the sleeping bag. 'Quick, get in.'

I knew it was too late. The effect would be very fast. Sobbing, I crawled in beside her, taking her in my arms, her head on my shoulder. I felt her warmth, her breathing, and I said to myself, *At this moment she is still alive. I'll embed this moment in my memory forever. I'll keep her with me.*

Raewyn, I want you to know that it was a beautiful place, and that Leah chose it. The delicate fronds of the tree fern made a lace bed-hanging. Our ceiling was the fading evening sky. Light and shade dappled her face, moving in the breeze, like water. The stream gushed over its rocks. It was both peaceful and unbearable.

Leah managed a few more words, though they were slurred. She was like a surgical patient who's received a general anaesthetic and is swiftly, gratefully going under. She asked me to take care of you.

I said, *I will, of course I will.* I felt her press her mouth to my chest. She was thanking me for something, but her words became unintelligible and within seconds she fell silent.

I've seen many, many people go through the process of dying. I dreaded that Leah might suffer—fitting, vomiting, suffering pain or fear—but I'm sure she lost consciousness peacefully and without regret.

I told her that I loved her. I told her that the world was better for having had her in it, that she'd never be forgotten. I listened to her breathing become fainter and slower. I knew her systems were shutting down, that she was sliding into a coma. I knew that death would likely follow within an hour.

At this time, a morepork called from somewhere very close by, and another answered. I had a strange sensation—brought on, I suppose, by emotional trauma. I felt as though the whole earth was murmuring, was singing in a register too low for human ears. I sensed the vibrations through the ground. I felt comforted, as though by the arms of a mother. I can't think of another way to describe it.

I'm not a spiritual person, Raewyn. You know that. After my sister died, I developed an implacable hatred of any religion. Time after time, patients have asked me whether I believe in life after death. I used to duck the question because the answer was a resounding 'no'.

The scientist in me is certain that my sensations, as Leah's life ebbed away, were physiological phenomena—entirely explicable, not at all supernatural. It's very common for the recently bereaved to report delusions and magical thinking. Perhaps the wonder of it is that the human body has such useful tricks up its sleeve. The brain has coping mechanisms to soften the horrors of traumatic experience. It needs these mechanisms, or humanity wouldn't have survived. This is what I told myself, as I listened to the earth singing and the owls calling to one another.

And yet. And yet. I have never quite shaken the feeling that Leah and I were not alone at the moment of her death, that she was met and escorted on her way. It seemed utterly inconceivable that such a brilliant flame had been extinguished. I've never thought of the Ruahine Range in quite the same way since. The wise woman was kind to me that night. Wishful thinking, of course.

There came a time when I knew she was gone. I checked with great care, but I knew. I lay still, holding her as death began to change her body, and heavy clouds blotted out the stars. I didn't expect ever to sleep again, and it's true that I've been insomniac since that night. When I turn out the light, I relive that terrible moment when she took the poison. I know she is leaving me. I feel my heart break. I feel *your* heart break, Raewyn. Sleep is for the innocent.

When the Pleiades cluster rose over the horizon, I knew dawn would soon follow. I sensed the softening of the darkness, the filigree patterns of the tree fern becoming a little more defined. The first birds began their sleepy cries. It was raining, gently but steadily. And my girl was in my arms. She really did seem to be at rest.

Leah had told me exactly what to do next. 'You won't be thinking straight.' She was right. I was a mess. I had a syringe and diamorphine in my bag, which she'd requested in case the pentobarbital didn't do its awful job. My first thought, when I realised that dawn was coming and I would soon have to leave her, was to use the diamorphine on myself. All I wanted was to stay with her.

But no. I honoured my promises. I followed her instructions to the letter.

Almost to the letter. I disobeyed in two small ways.

First, I built a cairn of rocks on the bank above our forest beach. I dug her tin water bottle into the top of it. If I'm lucky, and the winds and storms haven't washed them away, these will help me to know the place when I return there.

Second, her turquoise cap still lay beside her; the cap she'd used to distract me at the moment she swallowed the poison. I pulled it onto my own head. It was something of hers, with a few strands of her hair. Just something.

I sat beside her for a last moment. I kissed her, wailing as I said goodbye. Then I left her there, in the place she loved.

I have no clear memory of the next hours. I was out of my mind, sometimes shouting, sometimes sobbing. I know I slipped and fell into Whio stream many times, but I didn't care. Somehow, I got myself back to Biddulph Road. I was staggering along it in the mud and rain when I saw a pick-up truck. There were people in the cab, cigarette smoke pouring out of one of the windows. I didn't bother to try to avoid them. Part of me wanted to be caught. I simply walked past. I now know that they were the three men who saw a hiker, wearing a turquoise hat beneath the hood of a jacket. They were telling the truth. That person was me.

When I reached my car at last, I changed back into respectable doctor-at-conference clothes. Then there was nothing else to do but to drive home, to claim I had a raging dose of flu and shut myself away. I was catatonic, vomiting, barely able to function. I knew you would call, and of course you did. And then began the cruel charade of searching for Leah. I threw myself into it. I almost persuaded myself that the whole thing was a nightmare, and we'd find her alive and well.

I have kept my promise to her. I have kept her secret. And yes, it was despicable never to have told you. And yes, I am a coward. You and Ira have been my friends, my family. You've lived with unremitting grief because of my actions, my lies, my treachery. I don't expect you to forgive me. Quite the opposite. I deserve your hatred. The greater the kindness you've shown, the deeper my shame and self-loathing. You, Leah and Helen—three women I've loved deeply, who were better people than me. I have failed you all.

I haven't yet been back to our valley, but I have sometimes hiked *almost* there, in order to be near her and to ensure that I still remember the route. I hope to make the journey for the last time one day soon. I plan to join Leah.

Thank you for your steadfast friendship. I am bitterly sorry to have betrayed it.

With my love,

Felix

Postscript

My will is lodged with Todd Tillerson. Arapito homestead will be sold and the proceeds distributed among my children, along with the rest of my estate. The Arapito land, however, is for Ira. Please persuade him to accept it. Had I married Leah, as in my mind and heart I did, then it would be hers upon my death. Paratas have farmed that land for fifty years. Ira has cared for me, quietly and tactfully: piles of firewood have arrived, lawns have been magically mown, the water pump rebuilt, the well deepened, the drive regraded, my car's battery jump-started whenever I've left the lights on overnight (which has been increasingly often), and a thousand other services unobtrusively rendered. He is more than family.

Felix

THIRTY-ONE

Gyp and Gloria had barged under the fence and were sniffing for rabbits in the wet grass of the paddock. Blissful ignorance. I roamed around the bleak rose beds, wondering what was happening in Raewyn's house right now.

I'd left them to read Dad's letters, along with the photos I'd included in the envelope. I didn't want to intrude as they learned all those terrible details about Leah's last moments; I didn't want to be there when they realised that Dad had betrayed them. He'd carried on a secret relationship with their beloved daughter and sister, had been involved in her death and—worst of all—had let them suffer all these years. He let Raewyn hope, let Ira despair.

I envy you, Leah once told me. And she meant it. I was on the brink of adventure with my life ahead of me, while hers was over. It was her last day. She bought chocolate to take away the bitterness of the poison. She dropped it as she opened the door, stooped swiftly to pick it up. Yet Leah was never clumsy.

Cloud drooped on the snow-covered peaks like an oversized cap, sliding down their scarred faces, settling in the valleys. I hoped he'd found his cairn of stones and her tin water bottle.

I imagined him sitting by their waterfall, talking to her as hypothermia did its work. I wasn't grieving for him. Not yet. There was too much to think about; there was too much to decide.

Nathan called. It was strange to be standing in the icy dawn, knowing that my son was sleepless in an Indonesian night. He said he'd stayed up late, looking online for the quickest way to get to New Zealand.

'Definitely not,' I told him firmly. 'I'd love to see you, but no. Don't ruin your time of freedom and travel. You never know when these opportunities will come again.'

'But poor Grandpa! I should be helping to look for him.'

'I don't think he wants to be found, Nathan.'

'Why not?'

'Well . . . it's just a feeling I've got. I think he might already be dead. By choice.'

'By *choice*?' Nathan sounded incredulous.

'He dreaded losing control of himself, having to go into a rest home. I'm starting to wonder whether he's taken matters into his own hands. And that's okay, isn't it?'

I imagined the young man trying to visualise something so far outside his experience.

'I guess,' he said in the end. 'It's his life.'

As our call ended, Dave Perry was rumbling up the drive in a LandSAR vehicle full of volunteers. Good people, giving their own time.

'No news?' he called to me, as he opened his door.

I glanced at the cloud-covered mountains. I'd give Dad a head start, at least. What was one more lie among so many?

'No news,' I said.

•

The search net was widening. Volunteers drove up the tracks into the forest park but came back shaking their heads. And still I heard nothing from Raewyn or Ira.

Midmorning, Jodie Palmer took a call: a waitress had noticed a man sitting by himself in a café in Palmerston the day before. He seemed 'a bit lost' as she served his hot chocolate and scone.

'It's a long shot,' Jodie warned me. 'But he fits the description, and your dad could conceivably have hitched a lift to Palmy. They're going to check for CCTV images of him. Shouldn't be too long.'

It took almost an hour for the photos to arrive. My mind was up in the dripping trees, the cloud cover. Part of me wanted to believe Dad had simply set off on an adventure—hitching a ride to Palmerston, hot chocolate and a scone, perhaps somehow staying in a motel. But if it was him in that café, then I'd *really* messed up. I'd opened the envelope before his death. I'd caused incalculable harm.

'Here we are,' said Jodie, handing me her phone. 'This him?'

An elderly man in a rust-coloured jacket, with a fine head of white hair. Not Dad. This was somebody else's father. I shook my head. Disappointment. Relief.

'Sorry,' said Jodie. 'But the next call could be the one.'

As it turned out, my phone was the next to ring. It was Ira, and he wasn't wasting words.

'You should come over. Got things to talk about.'

•

Raewyn's kitchen table had seen it all.

Ira and I used to lounge here, noisily munching Anzac biscuits, way back in those sunshine days before the pitiless hammer of Huntington's smashed the Parata family. This was where Raewyn and Manu held hands while Dad broke the news of Manu's diagnosis. It was the scene of thousands of family meals, a father missing his mouth while his children pretended not to notice. Leah sat here to write her fake log, to drink that last cup of tea with her mum. The courage of that! It was on this table that

Raewyn laid out pumpkin soup, ready for the cold tramper who was due home any minute. This was where we gathered while searchers combed the mountains for a woman who was already dead. And now its worn surface was witness to the truth.

Raewyn was slumped over it, her face pressed into her folded arms, still wearing her nightdress and jersey. The pages of Dad's letter lay scattered around her. I hovered, feeling the weight of my family guilt.

'I'm so sorry,' I said. Weak, weak words.

Ira stood with his hands on the edge of the sink, staring out of the window. The tap drip-dripped into an overflowing metal bowl.

'Oh, Emily, you're here,' Raewyn murmured, raising her head to look at me. Her face was blotchy, her eyes unfocused. A strand of hair had stuck to her cheek.

'Ira called me,' I said.

'What do you think of all this? We . . . we're . . .'

Her face was collapsing, her mouth twisting into a bitter, smiling grimace. Tears washed down her cheeks, into her hair.

'Running out of tears,' she managed to gasp. 'Both of us.'

I pulled a chair close, trying to put my arms around her, still parroting platitudes about how sorry I was.

'We thought she'd been tested!' she wailed. 'Negative! We celebrated, we were so happy for her. Now I know, I can see the signs, I can see everything she was hiding from me. The baggy clothes, the big smile, all that pretending . . . I said she was working too hard, she needed feeding up . . . oh, my darling, my—'

Grief drowned her words. Behind her, I saw Ira press his upper arm across his eyes, his powerful body heaving with sobs. Twenty-five years after her death, they were finally mourning for Leah.

'Felix,' whispered Raewyn. 'Any sign of Felix?'

Despite everything, she was still asking about Dad. I'd expected her to curse him.

'No sign,' I said.

'Are you going to show the police all of this?'

'I think that's up to you.'

She tried to wipe her face with her hands, tried to clear her throat. She picked up the photograph of Leah by the stream.

'This is the place where she died, isn't it? The place where she is right now. A valley that rings with birdsong. I'm glad he was with her at the end. I'm glad she wasn't alone. But . . . why not tell me? You should have told me, Leah.' She bent to kiss Leah's smiling face in the photo. 'Why didn't you tell me, silly girl? That hurts. That hurts. You know I would have taken care of you. I'd have done anything for you.'

Ira spoke without shifting his gaze from the window. 'She'd made up her mind, Mum. She'd seen Dad go through it.'

'She might have had years, though,' Raewyn protested. 'I know how those years can be rich and full of love. They could have had a life together, even if it wasn't a long one. They'd have packed more into a few years than most people do into eighty! It must seem strange to you, Emily, being his daughter, but it's not strange to me.'

She reached for the picture of Dad chopping firewood outside a hut, and held it side by side with the one of Leah.

'I knew he loved her,' she said.

'You knew about them?'

'Well, no, but . . . he was in love with her. I could just tell. And the way she talked about him, the way she carefully *didn't* talk about him. I wondered whether one day they might . . . the gossips would have judged them, of course, but I didn't care about their ages. I knew he was broken when we lost her. My Leah had changed him. And ever since, grieving for her has been a bond between us.'

'You're not disgusted with him?'

Before she could answer, a hissing exhalation from Ira had me glancing around.

'What do you think? Christ! Up at the bivvy that day, when I was hearing echoes, he came over all fatherly, all caring—and he'd snuck up there and left that fucking note on the table! He knew she'd never been near the place, he knew she'd been dead three days. All these years, I've been grateful to him. All these years, he knows I've kept on looking for her. And now I've got to forget and forgive, have I? *That's okay, mate, you lied to me, you left my sister to rot in the mountains, these things happen.*'

'He did what she asked of him,' said Raewyn. 'He did it faithfully, though it nearly destroyed him, and he's had to live with it. He's never slept since.'

'Never got to say goodbye to her,' muttered Ira. 'Never got to bring her home, never . . . never . . .' He seemed to stagger a little, as though an earthquake was rocking the ground beneath his feet. 'How long have you known, Emily?'

'He gave me that envelope the day I arrived here,' I said. 'He asked me to look after it. I honestly thought it was his will. I opened it at four o'clock this morning.'

Not a lie.

'Why did you bring it to us?'

'Because of what he said in the letter. Truth matters. The instructions were that I could open it after his death. And I think that's now.'

Raewyn murmured something, reaching out to me.

'It's okay,' I told her. 'I mean, it's not okay at all. I'm worried about whether he suffered, whether he was frightened. But this was his choice. He once asked me to help him have a good death.'

'A good death?'

'Yes. And I hope this is it.'

'We hope so too,' she said. 'We hope he found Leah.'

She clutched the photos, pressing them with her fingertips as though she might reach through time to touch her daughter.

The dripping of the tap into the bowl was the only sound in a long silence.

'I might have done what Leah did,' said Ira suddenly, 'if I knew Huntington's had come for me. It's not crazy to choose to fall asleep up in the ranges while you've got the chance. You don't get a choice later on, that's the problem. She did it while she could. And if you'd known, Mum, you would have used every trick in the book to stop her.'

'I wouldn't have wanted her to leave us.'

Ira straightened—groaning, 'God, what a mess,' flexing his shoulders up and down. He briefly laid an arm around his mother's shoulder before flinging himself into a chair at the table. 'Can I see those again?' he asked her, holding out his hand for the photos.

I watched as he looked through them.

'D'you think Dad could have made it to their little valley?' I asked.

'We do think so,' said Raewyn. 'Don't we, Ira? We're sure he's been planning all of this for a long, long time.'

'But he'll have been on foot,' I pointed out. 'Walking from here to Biddulph Road, then all the way up to this Whio stream, and then the hard part—several hours' really steep climbing through the bush, with no trails. That's a tough hike for anyone, isn't it?'

Ira was looking at the picture of his sister, with her feet in the water.

'Very tough,' he said, 'But he probably wasn't carrying anything, he's kept himself fit, and he once knew all this country like the back of his hand. Remember, he won't have gone along the roads, not if he was on foot—he'll have taken the short cut across the farm and up the Arapito ravine, comes out on Biddulph Road. Much, much quicker. That explains why nobody spotted him.'

'But his memory's so bad. Wouldn't he get lost?'

'Better in the morning, though. Right? And his long-term memory is still pretty good—he's often sharper than I am when it comes to details about the past. It sounds as though he and Leah made this trip often. He knew it well.'

Raewyn had gone to wash her face at the sink and was drying it on a hand towel. She'd obviously decided that the time for tears had passed, at least for now.

'Felix was Felix,' she said, rejoining us at the table. 'He'll have got everything ready while he still had all his faculties. He probably had his escape kit packed years ago. He will have drawn himself a map. He will have written out instructions a child could follow—exactly *what* he's doing and exactly *how* to get there. The timings, everything. That's how he copes, it's how he kept going so long. He's worked with people who have dementia. He knew how to communicate with his future self.'

I murmured agreement, thinking of the green box. *HER. REMEMBER!*

'I bet he put his directions in one of those plastic holders around his neck,' Raewyn was saying. 'Right there for him to see, in case he forgot what he was doing. We reckon he will have set out well before daybreak, maybe used a head torch at first. He'll have walked as fast and as far as he could while his mind was still clear. With a bit of luck—and a lot of perseverance—he will have got there in daylight.'

'Would he know the place, though?' I asked. 'Won't it have changed, after all this time?'

Ira laid the photo of Leah on the table, smoothing it with the palm of his hand. I could see the creases where Dad had crumpled it.

'The stream, the rocks, those things won't have shifted much,' he said. 'Your dad's marker cairn with the water bottle might still be there. Some of her things, her camping stove, tin plate, her . . . things that don't decay. They'll have been scattered, for sure, and bush will have grown up around them, but I bet some of it's still just lying there.' He glanced at Raewyn. 'I don't think there will be anything of Leah.'

'That's what she wanted,' said Raewyn.

In the silence, a text from Jodie arrived on my phone.

Hi Emily. No news sorry. Will be making press statement at 5 pm.

I stood up, trailing my hand along the table on my way to the door.

'Two nights in the ranges,' I said, looking across the battered landscape. 'He can't still be alive, can he?'

Out of the corner of my eye, I saw Ira shaking his head.

'With the wind chill, overnight temperatures up there will have been way below zero. That's a killer.'

'You hear of people surviving for weeks.'

'Not in winter. Anyway, that's people who have the right gear, find shelter and look after themselves. Doc Kirkland wasn't going to do that, was he? That wasn't his plan at all. My guess is he made a massive effort all day, got to where he was going—to Leah—and then he just lay down beside that stream. He might even have taken off his clothes. He was probably already dead when we met up at the petrol station, the night before last.'

The blue light. The little owl that called and called.

'I hope he's never found,' I said.

It hit me then. The first wave of grief. *My dad. My dad is dead.* Raewyn's chair scraped as she came to stand beside me, linking her arm through mine.

'We don't want Leah disturbed either. People won't even try to understand why she did it. They'll go crazy—*Ooh, what hot gossip! Leah Parata slept with Dr Kirkland! She talked him into stealing medicine and helping her to die!* Crowds of ghoulish death tourists will go looking for her bones. They'll find things of hers and keep them as souvenirs. They'll take photos, smoke cigarettes, smash down the bush. They'll chase away the bats and all those singing birds. Her peace will be destroyed.'

'Police file opened again,' growled Ira. 'Inquest. Jeez, can you imagine the circus?'

'What do we do?' I asked. 'All these people are looking for him. We can't just let them carry on, can we?'

Ira shrugged. 'The search won't go on for long, not at this level. They'll soon call it off. Chalk it up to dementia and hypothermia.'

'I'm sure wasting police time is a criminal offence.'

'What d'you want to tell them?' Ira gestured towards Dad's letter, scattered across the table. 'A man with Alzheimer's wrote something years ago, hinting he might go for a walk in the ranges some time. It's not what you'd call a rock-solid lead, is it?'

'But *we* know where he's gone.'

'Do we?' Ira was leaning back in his chair—arms folded, brows lowering. He seemed much more like his old, stubborn self. 'You show them this letter, and all anyone will be interested in is what went on between him and Leah, and whether he pressured her to kill herself, and how he got hold of the drugs, and how he lied about it forever after. The papers, the TV, the radio—they'll be like dogs scrapping over a bone.'

'You're right,' I conceded reluctantly. 'But a lot of good people are giving their own time.'

'Those people have been strolling up and down my farm for the past two days, going home to warm beds every night. They'd much rather that than hauling themselves across streams full of freezing snowmelt, bivvying overnight in a blizzard. If you really want to make them miserable and put them in danger, send them up there. And I bet they still wouldn't find him.'

Raewyn looked up at me, squeezing my arm. 'Emily, don't forget that Felix did search and rescue for years. He saved people, often up in the mountains in terrible conditions, putting his own life at risk. He gave, and gave, and gave. Well, maybe now he's calling in that debt. If you're asking us, we'd say please—*please*—leave him and Leah alone. Let them rest in peace.'

I didn't reply. I didn't need to. We three conspirators knew we'd be keeping our secret.

Rain was hosing across the landscape, but a vivid ribbon of cyan edged the snowy uplands. It looked just like those brush-wide streaks of bright blue sky I painted as a toddler.

'Where are they?' I asked.

Ira came to join us at the windows. He wasn't looking towards Biddulph's bivvy anymore. We were scanning the crumpled wilderness further south.

'I know where Whio stream comes out,' he said, 'but I've never tried to follow it. I've been searching for Leah in the wrong place all this time. Way, way out. There must be hundreds of those little gullies with streams, but I think she could be . . . see that sticking-up bluff, just to the north of that slip? Now follow it down, there's a spur to the left. Got it?'

'Got it,' I said doubtfully. 'I think.'

'Sharp spur, below the bluff. Follow the line of that spur—d'you see it's kind of crooked? You can just make out the creases coming off it . . . We can't know for sure, but I think Leah's valley could be one of those. Look at the third one down from the top of the spur; I'm pretty sure there's a running stream. The foliage is a slightly different colour. See?' He was pointing as I squinted along his arm. 'I think she's in there.'

I'm not sure whether he and I were looking at the same thread of foliage. All I could see was a crazed, snow-dusted network of spurs and slips, of countless pleats and folds. But I fixed on a point and told myself that was the place.

The three of us watched as the band of cyan glowed more and more brilliantly, lit by an invisible sun. And then, quite suddenly, it seemed as though the clouds were raining light onto Leah and Dad's valley.

In my mind, now and forever, that was my father's grave.

•

The search was scaled back incrementally as each day passed. Media reports of 'significant concerns' quickly evolved into 'losing hope'. Soon it entered what the press release called *limited continuous mode*, which amounted to calling it off. Dad's bank account hadn't been touched, and there had been no credible sighting of him.

'We'll keep looking,' Jodie assured me. 'The file isn't closed. If and when he turns up, he'll be identified.'

I thanked her, feeling guilty in every sense of the word. 'I don't think he's going to turn up,' I said. 'Not alive.'

She didn't argue.

•

They never found him. Not a boot, not a jacket, not a water bottle. He walked out of his home one night and vanished off the face of the earth.

THIRTY-TWO

I stayed in Tawanui until the summer. Long enough to begin the process of persuading the coroner to declare that Dad was presumed dead; long enough to sort through his things, to repaint Arapito homestead, to put it on the market. Long enough to cajole Ira into accepting Dad's bequest of the land and arrange for Todd Tillerson to handle the legalities. It was long enough to say goodbye to my father.

I often sat on the porch and imagined he was still here with me, the dogs snoozing at his feet, drinking coffee and playing chess. I talked to him.

'I hope you made it,' I said aloud, gazing up towards their sunlit valley. 'Did you make it, Dad?'

Raewyn and I disagreed on one point. I'd persuaded her to let me tell Todd, who was a staunch ally in the winding up of Dad's affairs, but she was also adamant that Carmen and Eddie must hear the whole story.

'He's their father too,' she pointed out. 'They have a right.'

'But perhaps they'd rather not know. It's shattering, it changes everything. I really do think Eddie was crazy about Leah. How hurt and betrayed is he going to feel? She didn't love him—she loved his father! I just don't know how he'll react. Maybe it's cruel to put him through that? And I can imagine Carmen going off the deep end, trying to have Dad's body found and brought down for a "proper" funeral.'

I was in Raewyn's kitchen. I spent a lot of time at her place nowadays. Arapito seemed too empty.

'Give them the truth,' she insisted, watching as I poured tea from her brown clay pot. 'You and I, we don't own it. Nobody does. What they do with it is up to them.'

'Okay, you win.' I puffed out my cheeks, thinking gloomily about the logistics. 'But I hope it doesn't lead to disaster. Should I drive up and visit them, sit them down together and break the news? Or phone them? Or a video call? Whatever I do, there's going to be one hell of a scene.'

Tears were welling in Raewyn's eyes. She took Dad's letter out of her pocket, unfolded it, refolded it. I was sure she knew every word by heart.

'It's Felix's story,' she said. 'His and Leah's. I think you should let him tell it, in his own words. That's how he told you and me.'

So I made two copies of Dad's confession. Raewyn and I wrote a covering note of our own, warning Carmen and Eddie that they might find it extremely disturbing. We urged them to read it in a private moment when they had plenty of time. We explained that we desperately wanted the story to remain untold.

Then I gathered the letter and copies of the photographs, along with the contents of their respective childhood memory boxes, and posted everything to my siblings' homes.

'We'd better get our tin hats on,' I advised Raewyn as we left the post office. 'We've just lit the charge. Prepare for the bomb to go off.'

She looked worried, pretending to don a hat. 'My grand-mother had a favourite proverb,' she said. '*Truth and roses have thorns about them*. I think she'd quoting it now.'

I was wrong. I misjudged my siblings.

Carmen phoned me the evening after her parcel arrived. I'd never heard my sister sound so stunned, so subdued.

'It's just impossible to take in,' she whispered, her voice cracking. 'I can't believe it. I can't. I've been for a long walk, I've talked to Richard—don't worry, he won't tell anyone; nobody wants Dad's memory ripped to shreds. I can't get my head around . . . but in a weird way, it makes perfect sense, doesn't it? Dad! We never knew him, did we?'

'I don't think we did.'

'My wedding day, my bloody wedding day! None of us had a clue. No wonder he was crying in the car. I mean, imagine the agony they were both going through. Leah wished me all the happiness in the world, she caught my bouquet. I said she'd be next to get married, and all the time she was planning her own death. I can't believe . . .'

She wanted to talk it through, over and over, round and round. I understood. I felt much the same.

'So they're together again now?' she asked in the end. 'Up in the bush, by this lovely little waterfall?'

'I think so. I really do. We don't know exactly where it is, but Ira has gone up some of the way. He seems certain Dad will have made it.'

'Good. Let's leave them up there. I hope they're at peace.'

Eddie's reaction was still more surprising. It consisted of a brief but polite email, thanking me for the contents of his memory box. He didn't mention Dad's letter; he didn't mention Leah. Not a syllable. At the time I gave a mental shrug, grateful that nobody was demanding to call the police, or send search parties up to recover Dad's body.

When it came to clearing out the house, Carmen put up her hand for the grandmother clock, along with a van full of paintings and furniture. Eddie wanted only two things: Dad's desk, and his leather office chair.

'It's how I remember him,' he said, as we stood in the study, surrounded by Dad's chaos. 'Working. That was all he ever did, wasn't it? That's who he was. He worked.'

I couldn't stand it. I had to know what was going on in my brother's mind. 'Did you ever look inside that parcel I sent you?' I asked.

'What parcel? Oh yes.' He lifted one shoulder. 'I had a swift glance through before chucking it out. It was just certificates and things. I try not to collect clutter.'

'But . . . I mean, you must have read Dad's letter?'

He looked blank. 'Letter?'

He was lying. I knew that studied innocence, the rapid blinking, the way he couldn't meet my eye. I suspected the truth was unbearable to him, so he was pretending it had never happened. My brother has no qualms about rewriting history. He tries not to collect clutter.

•

Ira and Cathy had relocated a rather beautiful villa onto the site of the single man's quarters. Cathy ensured it was perfectly positioned to make the most of the views she so admired. The old house arrived on the back of a massive lorry, like a giant tortoise. We all had a fine time, watching a bulldozer dragging the tortoise up that steep track, and soon our bus shelter was in use once again. It was fun to see Sean and Alex sitting on the wooden seat with their curly heads, their legs swinging as the bus ground its dusty way towards them. Dad would have liked that. If Cathy knew the shelter was once a secret postbox, she gave no sign of it.

Raewyn threw herself into the role of best step-grandmother in the world: she baked and read stories, flew kites, drove small people to their swimming lessons and play dates. Week after week, rain or shine, she stood on a touchline with plates of chopped-up apple, cheering miniature soccer players—until the summer, when they turned into miniature cricketers.

I went along to watch them play on my very last weekend in Tawanui. Sean came scooting up to Raewyn midway through the game, slapping her hand in a high five. He had boundless energy.

'Did you see my cool catch, Raewyn?'

'I saw it!' cried Raewyn. 'You're the champ.'

He slapped Cathy's hand too, and Ira's, and mine. Once the game had begun again, I snuck a piece of apple from Raewyn's half-time plate.

'I'm glad you phoned me that day,' I said to her. 'And bullied me.'

'You only came home for three weeks.'

'Can't get rid of you,' grumbled Ira. 'Bad penny.'

I bit into the apple. It came from one of the trees in Raewyn's orchard—the gnarled one over by the fence, next to the plum. I'd tasted its tangy fruit in countless pies and crumbles over the years. That old tree might outlive us all.

'Why don't you stay?' asked Cathy, who was standing with her arm around Ira's neck. 'At least give yourself another summer.'

'Oh, so tempting.'

'That's settled, then! Better cancel your flight.'

My old life seemed flat and vague, a faded painting in the back of a cupboard. Yet within days I'd be unlocking my own front door and stepping back into that life—if I could still remember how to lead it. I'd dust off my glad rags for our launch of *Admiral Flufflebum and the Christmas Kitten*; I'd be taking Toby to a pantomime, heading up to Yorkshire for Christmas with Mum. I'd see 2020 in with Sarah, who was throwing a party to celebrate the new decade. During January I'd be running some art workshops in a women's refuge, and working on the design of Admiral Flufflebum SNAP! cards.

And in February, I was to meet Nathan at Heathrow. A red-letter day! Nathan and Ella, still together after all their travels. Ah, well. Worse things could befall him. Life was moving on.

Beyond the town, the Ruahines shimmered and danced. They called to me. But by this time next week, I'd be gone.

•

My flight landed at five o'clock in the morning. Still dark. Rain spattered on the windows as we taxied across the wet tarmac. 'Welcome to Heathrow Airport,' said the co-pilot. He sounded miserable.

I'd left New Zealand just as Hawke's Bay began to luxuriate in another glorious summer; just as the first reports were coming in from Wuhan, China, about a mysterious virus that might or might not prove to be a global problem. Probably not. It'd most likely just fizzle out.

London was in Christmas mode, festooned with coloured lights and flashing reindeer and all kinds of fabulous kitsch. I took the tube from Heathrow, battling though the rush-hour throng, hauling my case down the road to my flat, fumbling for the key as I approached the drycleaners. I unlocked my own front door for the first time in almost a year. Locks? Who needs locks?

Opened it, slammed it shut behind me, trudged up my narrow staircase.

And here I am. Standing on my own landing.

The flat was silent. Ursula would be at work; Fran had found another place. I floated, letting my mind adjust to the alien normality. A distant siren, voices from the street, the hum of a plane. Sandalwood in Ursula's potpourri, starch from the laundry below, spices from the Thai restaurant on the corner.

I missed the company of Gyp and Gloria, who'd been adopted by Raewyn. I missed the Arapito grandmother clock, ticking and chiming her gentle way through hours and days. As I dragged my case into my bedroom, its wheels caught on a threadbare piece of carpet. *Need to fix that.* Grey skies filled the window. Grey roofs. Tower blocks in the distance, leafless trees in the little park. No shimmering mountains, no gilded haze, no flaxes or foliage along the Arapito stream, no Ira moving stock across the paddocks, no white-haired man setting up his beloved chessboard.

I was taking off my jacket when a solid, four-footed figure came trotting in to rub his cheek against my legs, with little rearing hops of delight.

'Max,' I murmured, bending to pick up the purring bundle. 'You haven't changed a bit, mate.'

That's when I saw the parcel on my bed. A cardboard box, large, quite heavy. Ursula must have signed for it and left it there. I felt the old excitement as I fetched a knife from the kitchen and slid it through the masking tape, pulling out handfuls of shredded packing paper.

And there they were, exactly as I expected yet—always— somehow even more precious: a stack of pristine copies of *Admiral Flufflebum and the Christmas Kitten*, by Sarah Massey, illustrated by Emily Kirkland.

Sitting on the edge of my bed, stroking Max with one hand, I turned the pages of a living, breathing story. The magic of this moment had never worn off. Holding the first copies of a new book still felt like a miracle.

Sarah had dedicated it, as she always did, to her husband and children. I hadn't.

To Felix Kirkland
My waymark

THIRTY-THREE

Soon after Christmas, a Norwegian couple made contact with the police in New Zealand. They'd been on a motoring holiday in the country back in June, before moving on to Australia. They'd only just heard from a friend about the missing person in Hawke's Bay.

The story they told was this: around the time that Dr Kirkland disappeared, they had parked their hired campervan up a very rough track in the Ruahine forest area. They'd since established that this was Biddulph Road. They spent the night pulled up on a verge, during which time they saw and heard nobody.

The following morning, they were getting ready to leave when a hiker appeared, walking briskly towards the mountains. He wore his map in a clear plastic pocket around his neck. The couple were feeling woebegone after a miserably cold night in the unheated van, so they asked him where they could get breakfast and good coffee. He seemed uncertain for a moment, but then said he thought there was an excellent café on the main street in Tawanui.

He asked them about their journey. The Norwegians were on an extended honeymoon, and the hiker congratulated them 'with great politeness and enthusiasm', they said. They found him charming and offered him a lift to the start of his trail, which he gratefully accepted. They drove for a few minutes—perhaps five or six kilometres, they thought—until the track crossed a wooden plank bridge, and here he asked them to stop. He thanked them cheerfully, wishing them a happy life together as he hopped down from the van. They last saw him setting off up the stream, which was quite a torrent. They drove on a little further before finding a safe place to turn their vehicle around. By the time they crossed the bridge again, the hiker was out of sight.

The police emailed them a photograph of my father, and they responded immediately. *Yes! That is the guy we saw. He's even wearing the same jacket.*

Upon questioning, they agreed that they'd wondered whether it was a good idea for a not-so-young man to be heading into the mountains in midwinter. But he seemed confident and well-equipped, and he plainly knew the country very well.

Besides, he'd assured them, he wasn't going to be alone. He had arranged to meet a friend up there. She'd gone on ahead. She was waiting for him. He would be with her by nightfall.

Acknowledgements

Not long before I began to write this story, I found myself unexpectedly and hurriedly moving from Hawke's Bay to Wellington for what turned out to be a couple of years. For various reasons this was an intense time for me and mine, but it was made easier—and ultimately lovely—by the kindness of strangers. There were many, but special thanks to Phillip and Robyn upstairs, to Liberty Justice, and to the author-friendly crew at Picnic Café in the glorious Rose Garden, at whose tables hundreds of hours were spent and much of this book was written. A shout-out to far-flung family too, especially Anne Wallace and Julia Dickens, for all the cheering parcels, phone calls and care.

And thank you, Wellington. I'll miss the magic of waking to the cries of kaka in the misty forest of the town belt outside my back door. My apartment windows looked towards the parliament building, floodlit at night, whose flag was lowered in mourning after the Christchurch terror attack and eruption of Whakaari. The city was my home when Covid-19 appeared on the scene, changing the world in ways most of us could never have imagined. Hugs to Cora Meredith and Paul Harrison, the best lockdown companions ever, who put up with my dancing about to Abba and taught me to play Catan.

The writing of a novel is only one aspect of its creation; I'd be sunk without the help of an army of skilled people. I'm constantly grateful to Jane Gregory and her team at David Higham Associates, especially Stephanie Glencross, the first person ever to read this story, for her transformative advice. Heartfelt thanks to Annette Barlow at Allen & Unwin for absolutely everything, to Angela Handley for expertly steering the entire process, to Ali Lavau for superb editorial input and Christa Munns for meticulous proofreading; to Clare Drysdale, Kate Ballard and all in London, and Melanie Laville-Moore and the team in Auckland. Despite the challenges posed by the pandemic, including working from home, all have been pillars of steadiness and calm.

A mention in despatches for my father, staunch champion of these stories I keep writing—thanks Dad!—and for my brothers and sisters: Stephen, Hetta, Julia, James, Sarah and Paul. I haven't seen any of you while writing *Remember Me*, except in those hilarious little Zoom boxes. Trust me, guys—this story is fiction, these characters are entirely imaginary. Carmen and Eddie aren't based on any of you, who are of course marvellous in every possible way. So there'll be no need to throw me out of the family WhatsApp group, okay?

To Tim, who held the fort, and George, Sam and Cora: thanks for being exactly who you are. I am so very lucky.